GRADED GO PROBLEMS

FOR BEGINNERS

VOLUME FOUR

ADVANCED PROBLEMS

by

Kano Yoshinori 9-dan

The Nihon Ki-in

Published by
The Nihon Ki-in
7-2 Gobancho
Chiyoda-ku, Tokyo
Japan

Distributed by The Ishi Press, Inc.
CPO Box 2126, Tokyo, Japan

In North America order from:
THE ISHI PRESS INTERNATIONAL
1400 Shoreline Blvd., Building A7
Mountain View, California 94043

First Printing April 1990
Printed in Japan

Table of Contents

Preface

This is the fourth and final volume of the series *Graded Go Problems for Beginners* and is aimed at the 10- to 15-kyu player. The problems here are more difficult than the ones in volume three and if you could solve problems of the same level of difficulty during your own games, your strength would be higher than 10-kyu.

The answers to many of these problems are a bit terse, but we are assuming that that many of the elementary tactics covered in the first three volumes have been learned by the reader. One reason for the brevity of the answers is to encourage the readers to think out all the other possible variations and to assure themselves that the solutions presented do lead to the desired result. The reader should attempt to 'refute' the correct answer until he knows beyond a doubt that the correct answer does in fact work. By pondering each problem in this way, the reader will develop an instinct for finding the winning move in his games.

Kano Yoshinori 9-dan
March 1990

Glossary

atari — check, i.e. a move threatening to capture on the next move.

dame — neutral points which profit neither Black nor White.

dan — rank given to players to indicate their strength at the game. When a player's strength improves after attaining the rank of 1-kyu, he is promoted to amateur 1-dan and as he becomes stronger, the numerical value of his *dan* increases. The top amateur dan rank is usually 6-dan. The professional dan ranks start at 1-dan and go up to 9-dan, which is the highest rank attainable. A professional 1-dan is usually about two stones stronger than an amateur 6-dan. See *kyu*.

double atari — giving atari to two different stones or groups of stones at the same time.

eye — a point on the board which is surrounded by stones of the same color.

ko — a shape in which your stone is captured but it is illegal to retake the capturing stone even though you can occupy all of its liberties.

kyu — a rank given to players to indicate their strength at the game. Beginners are arbitarily classified at 30-kyu and as they become stronger, the numerical value of their *kyu* decreases. For example, 15-kyu is stronger than 20-kyu. See *dan*.

nakade — a large eye-space which, by skillful play, can be reduced to a single eye. (See explanation on page 222 of volume one of this series.)

oiotoshi — a move which gives atari to a group of stones in such a way that no matter how one defends, the group will still be in atari.

oshitsubushi — a shape in which you give atari to two or more of your opponent's stones in such a way that he cannot defend against this atari without committing suicide.

seki — an impasse or stalemate between groups: if one side tries to attack the other side's group, his own group is put into atari and dies. Therefore, neither side can attack or attempt to atari.

snapback — a tactic in which one stone is offered as a sacrifice and if it is taken, the capturing stones are in turn captured.

ADVANCED PROBLEMS

LEVEL ONE

SECTION 1. MIDDLE-GAME PROBLEMS

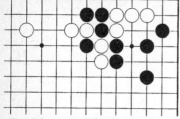

Problem 1. Black to play.

How should Black play to rescue his three stones at the top? All ladders are favorable for Black.

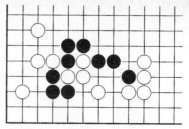

Problem 2. Black to play.

Black has a tesuji which enables him to capture three white stones.

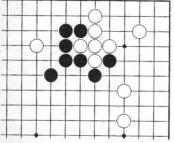

Problem 3. Black to play.

How should Black connect to ensure that the white groups at the top and bottom remain separated?

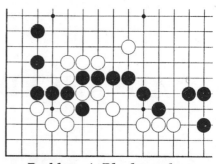

Problem 4. Black to play.

Black has a tesuji which will enable him to capture two white stones. Black's first move is important.

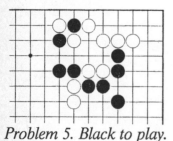

Problem 5. Black to play.

Black has to give up a stone at the top. What is the best way to sacrifice it?

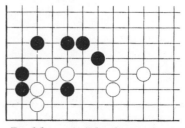

Problem 6. Black to play.

What is the best way to invade White's territory?

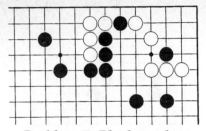

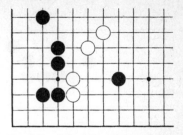

Problem 7. Black to play.
Black has a tesuji by which he can either rescue his isolated stone in the corner or prevent White from linking up his four at the center top.

Problem 8. Black to play.
Where is the vital point that robs White's stones of their base? Black best move is one that makes good shape.

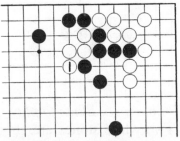

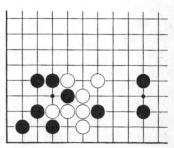

Problem 9. Black to play.
How should Black answer White 1? Black should mainly think about defending the shape of his own stones.

Problem 10. Black to play.
There is a black stone in atari. Should Black think about saving this stone or sacrificing it?

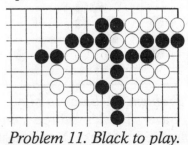

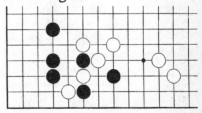

Problem 12. Black to play.
How can black link up his stones on the right to the ones in the corner? Don't let this situation turn into a ko.

Problem 11. Black to play.
Seven black stones are about to be cut off. Save them by sacrificing a stone.

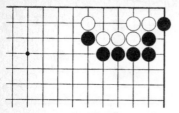

Problem 13. Black to play.
How should Black play in this position?

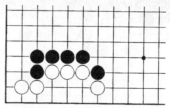

Problem 14. Black to play.
How should Black play? Note the similarities and differences between this position and that of Problem 13.

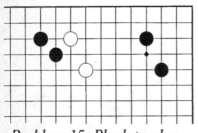

Problem 15. Black to play.
How should Black attack? You must play a move that robs White of his base.

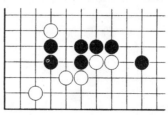

Problem 16. Black to play.
Two white stones are short of liberties. Attack them by striking at the vital point.

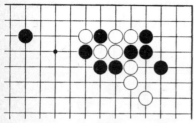

Problem 17. Black to play.
Black's three stones on the outside are weak. Your task is to destroy White's eye shape while eliminating the weakness of these three stones.

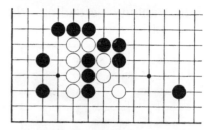

Problem 18. Black to play.
Save Black's three endangered stones. You must utilize the one black stone on the right.

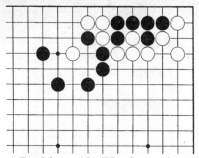

Problem 19. Black to play.
By using a 'squeeze' tesuji, you can capture the three white stones at the top and rescue six of Black's.

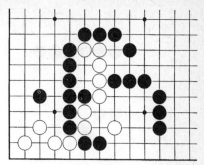

Problem 20. White to play.
White must save all of his surrounded stones as well as capture the two black stones at the bottom.

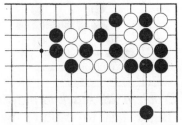

Problem 21. Black to play.
How should Black atari the three white stones at the top?

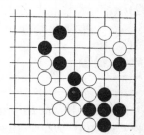

Problem 22. Black to play.
The black stones in the corner can live in sente.

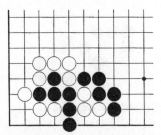

Problem 23. Black to play.
Black can capture the three white stones on the right in sente by sacrificing a stone.

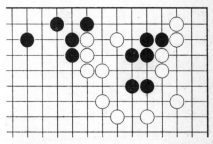

Problem 24. Black to play.
How should Black play so as to link up his two groups of stones?

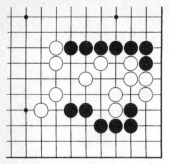

Problem 25. Black to play.
How should Black play so as to cut off six white stones from the center?

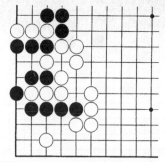

Problem 26. Black to play.
How should Black play so as to link up all his stones?

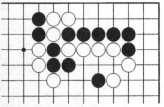

Problem 27. White to play.
How should White play so as to capture three black stones? White's second move is important.

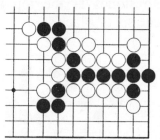

Problem 28. Black to play.
Black has to capture two white stones to rescue his nine stones on the right.

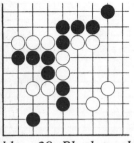

Problem 29. Black to play.
Black has to capture two white stones to save his four on the left.

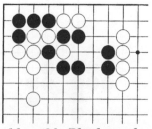

Problem 30. Black to play.
Capture White's two stones at the top and rescue the four black ones in the corner.

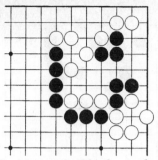

Problem 31. Black to play.
By sacrificing two stones, Black can capture three of White's in the center.

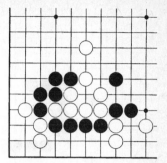

Problem 32. Black to play.
Capture six white stones.

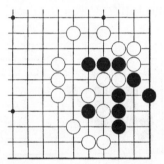

Problem 33. Black to play.
Capture two white stones and rescue the three isolated black stones in the center.

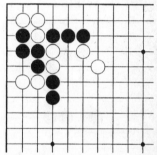

Problem 34. Black to play.
Black can link up his stones by capturing two white ones.

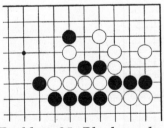

Problem 35. Black to play.
Capture the four white stones in the center.

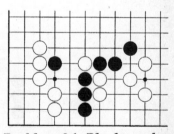

Problem 36. Black to play.
Black must capture a white stone to link up all of his.

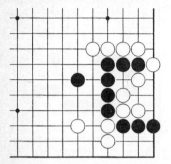

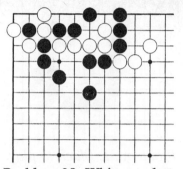

Problem 37. Black to play.
Black can rescue his three stones in the corner by capturing three of White's.

Problem 38. White to play.
How should White play so as to capture the black stones at the top?

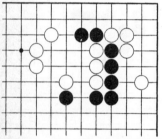

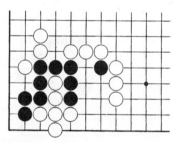

Problem 39. Black to play.
How should Black play so as to capture three white stones and rescue two of his own at the top?

Problem 40. Black to play.
Black to capture six white stones.

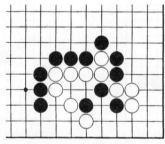

Problem 41. Black to play.
Black to capture six white stones.

SECTION 3. OPENING PROBLEMS

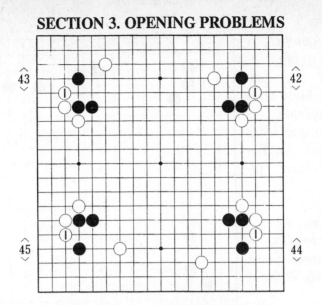

Problem 42, 43, 44, 45. Black to play.
In each of these corner position, White has played 1.
How should Black respond in each case?

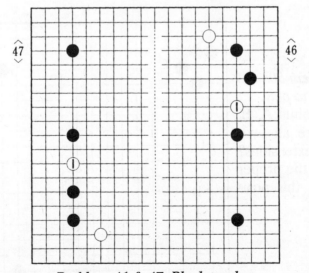

Problem 46 & 47. Black to play.
These two positions often arise in 6-stone handicap games.
How should Black answer White 1 in each?

Problem 48.
Black to play.
White has just played 1. How does Black respond?

This comes from a standard double-approach-move joseki.

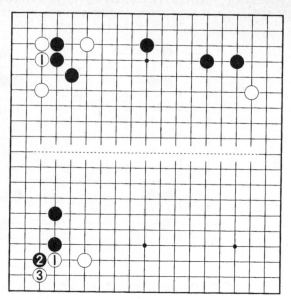

Problem 49.
Black to play.
How does Black respond to White 1 and 3?

Problem 50.
White to play.
The points A, B, and C are all two-space extensions? Which is the proper choice in this position?

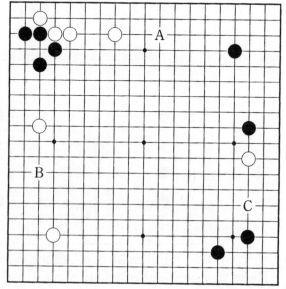

Problem 51.
Black to play.

From the three choices A, B, and C, which one is best? Hint: Are the two black stones at the bottom secure?

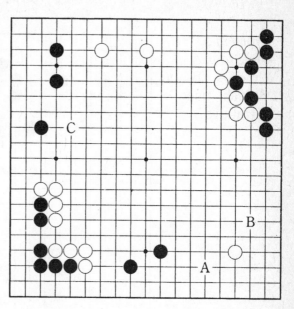

Problem 52.
White to play.

White A, B, or C. Which one is the correct choice?

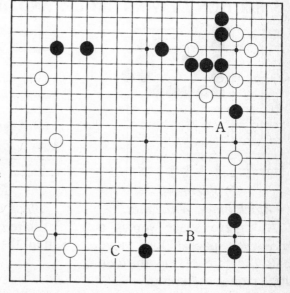

Problem 53.
White to play.
White A, B, or C? Which one is the best move?

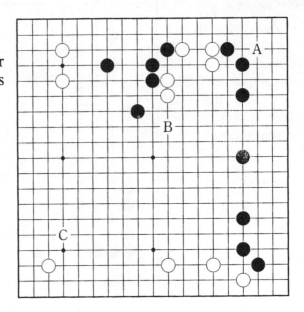

SECTION 3. LIVING GROUPS AND DEAD GROUPS

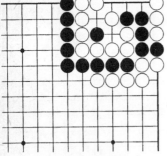

Problem 54.
Black plays, White dies.
A big-eye space versus a small-eye space. One move seals the fate of the thirteen white stones at the top.

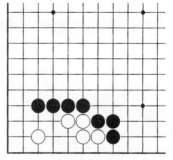

Problem 55.
Black plays, White dies.
White can't make two eyes. Kill all the white stones.

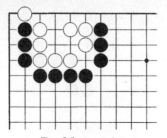

Problem 56.
Black plays, White dies.
Black can kill all the white stones, but be careful of seki.

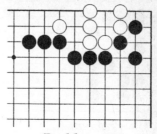

Problem 57.
Black plays, White dies.
By sacrificing a stone, Black can create a false eye on the left.

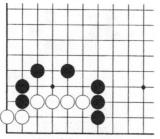

Problem 58.
Black plays, White dies.
The first move seals the fate of the white stones.

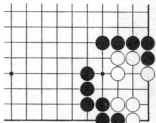

Problem 59.
Black plays, White dies.
Kill the white stones unconditionally.

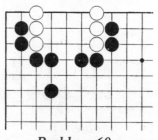

Problem 60.
White to play and live.
In a symmetrical position, play in the center. But which center point?

Problem 61.
White to play and live.
White can't capture two black stones until he has played on the vital point.

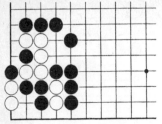

Problem 62.
White to play and live.
If White makes an eye in the corner, he can live.

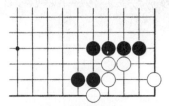

Problem 63.
White to play and live.
With one move, White can make an eye in two places.

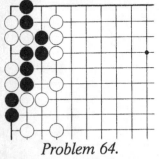

Problem 64.
Black to play and live.
To live, Black has to capture the three-stone and two-stone group at the same time.

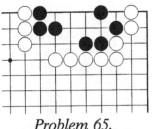

Problem 65.
Black to play and live.
By playing on the vital point, Black can immediately secure life.

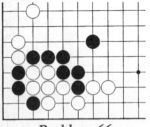

Problem 66.
Black to play and live.
By threatening to capture White by a shortage of liberties, Black can get two eyes for his stones in the corner.

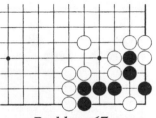

Problem 67.
Black to play and live.
The only way that Black can live is to create the 'under-the-stones' tesuji.

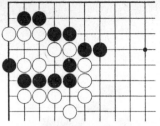

Problem 68.
Black plays and kills White.
By sacrificing a stone, Black can kill all the white stones in the corner.

Problem 69.
Black plays and kills White.
Black can unconditionally kill the white stones in the corner.

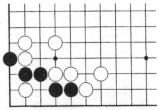

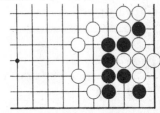

Problem 70.
Black to play and get a ko.
The only way Black can live is to create a ko.

Problem 71.
Black to play and get a ko.
If Black gets a ko, he will have succeeded.

SECTION 4. ENDGAME PROBLEMS

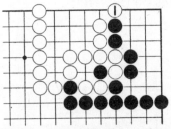

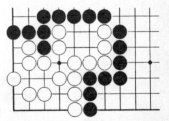

Problem 72. Black to play.
White has just played 1. Taking into account the corner and the two white stones in atari, what is the best way for Black to play.

Problem 73. Black to play.
There are two endgame points remaining. What is the most profitable way for Black to play?

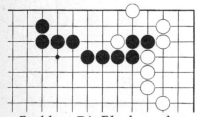

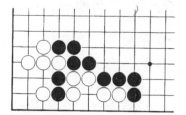

Problem 74. Black to play.
What is the most profitable way to stop the white intrusion at the top?

Problem 75. Black to play.
What is the best way to reduce White's territory?

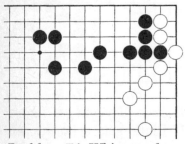

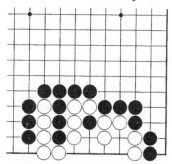

Problem 76. White to play.
How should White play in the corner for maximum gain?

Problem 77. Black to play.
There is a way that Black can capture the five white stones on the left.

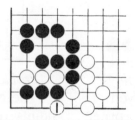

Problem 78. Black to play.
Assuming that there is no other more profitable points on the board, what is the best way for Black to respond to White 1?

ADVANCED PROBLEMS

LEVEL TWO

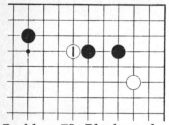

Problem 79. Black to play.
When White attaches with 1, there are three standard responses. What are they?

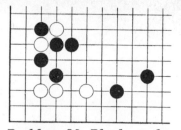

Problem 80. Black to play.
There is a good way to put pressure on the three white stones in the corner. Can you find it?

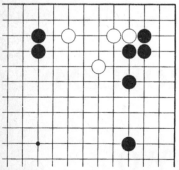

Problem 81. Black to play.
Black can profitably attack the white stones. Your aim should be to catch a stone.

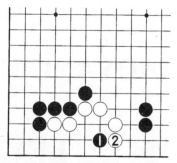

Problem 82. Black to play.
The exchange of 1 for 2 has just taken place. Black now has a good follow-up tesuji.

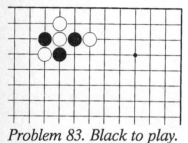

Problem 83. Black to play.
All the ladders are in Black's favor. What is his best move in this position?

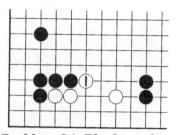

Problem 84. Black to play.
After White 1, how does Black keep up the pressure?

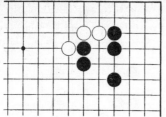

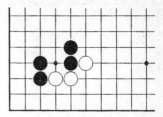

Problem 85. Black to play.
How does Black attack the three white stones?

Problem 86. Black to play.
How does Black attack in this position? Is there any difference between this position and the one in Problem 85?

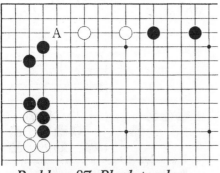

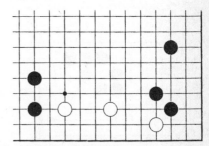

Problem 87. Black to play.
There is a stronger way than playing at A to attack White's stones at the top.

Problem 88. Black to play.
White's large-knight extension is a bit thin. Where should Black attack?

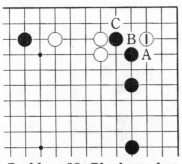

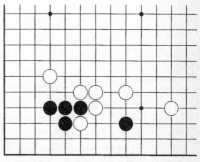

Problem 89. Black to play.
At which point — A, B, or C — should Black respond to White 1?

Problem 90. Black to play.
Black wants to link up his isolated stone to the ones on the left. How does he do this?

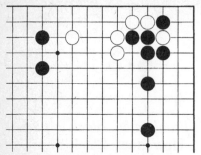

Problem 91. Black to play.
White's stones are vulnerable. How does Black attack them?

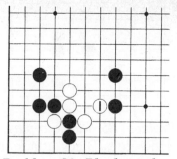

Problem 92. Black to play.
How does Black respond to White 1?

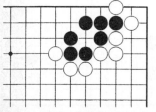

Problem 93. White to play.
How does White put pressure on the black stones?

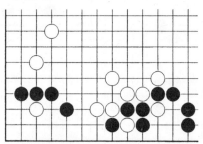

Problem 94. White to play.
White must first squeeze the black stones to the right. Then he can effectively attack Black's stones in the corner.

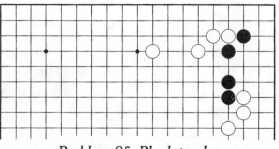

Problem 95. Black to play.
Black has to defend his corner. What is the best way for him to make eye shape?

Problem 96.
Black to play.
Which of the three points — A, B, or C — should White play? Keep in mind Black's thick position on the left.

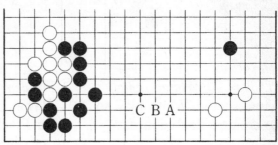

Problem 97.
Black to play.
Black has to connect his two stones in the top center. When he does so correctly, he will have two cutting points to aim at.

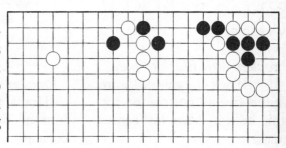

Problem 98.
Black to play.
Black has to defend his position at the bottom center? How can he do this in sente?

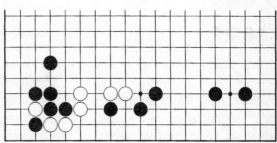

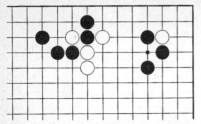

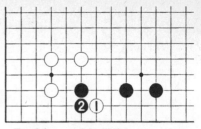

Problem 99. White to play.
How should White play so as to create a double threat?

Problem 100. White to play.
What is White's follow-up after Black plays 2? You have to sacrifice two stones.

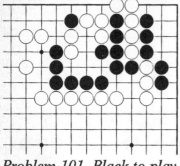

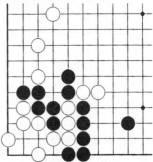

Problem 101. Black to play.
If Black can capture White's five stones on the top right, he can save his center stones.

Problem 102. Black to play.
How can Black capture four of White's stones in the corner?

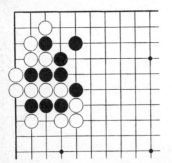

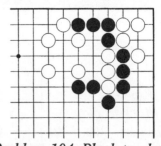

Problem 104. Black to play.
Black can capture three white stones and rescue his four at the top.

Problem 103. Black to play.
By sacrificing a stone, Black can capture five white ones and save three of his own.

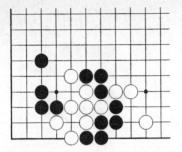

Problem 105. Black to play.
Unconditionally capture White's stones on the left.

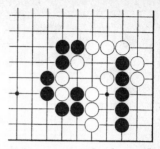

Problem 106. Black to play.
Cut off and capture White's three stones at the bottom.

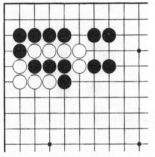

Problem 107. White to play.
Capture four black stones.

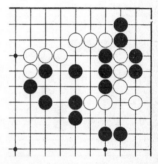

Problem 108. White to play.
Capture three black stones.

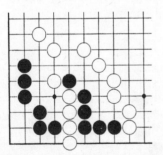

Problem 109. Black to play.
Cut off and capture White's four stones at the bottom.

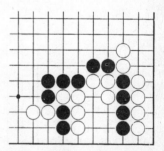

Problem 110. Black to play.
Black can capture three white stones and rescue four of his own on the right.

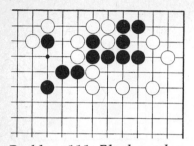

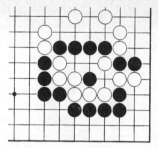

Problem 111. Black to play.
Black can capture three white stones and rescue his eight in the corner.

Problem 112. Black to play.
Rescue the four black stones in the center.

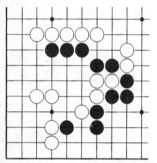

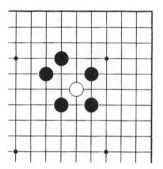

Problem 113. Black to play.
Capture three white stones in the center.

Problem 114. White to play.
The white stone is completely surrounded, but it can still escape.

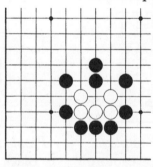

Problem 115. White to play.
The five white stones here can also escape.

Problem 116. **→**
Black to play.
How should Black attack the white group on the right after White has played 1?

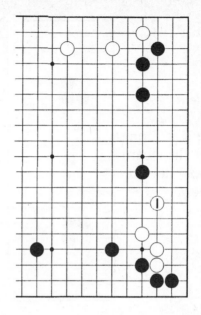

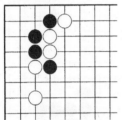

Problem 117.
Black to play.
White's shape is a bit unsatisfactory. How does Black attack?

Problem 118.
White to play.
Which of the two points — A or B — should White play?

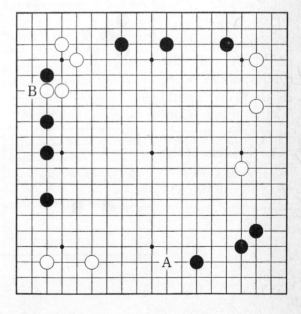

Problem 119.
Black to play.

There is one point on the board that has to be played now.

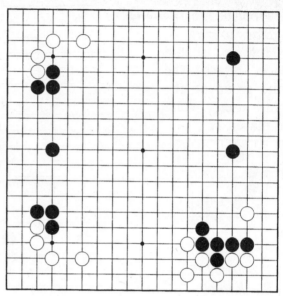

Problem 120.
White to play.

Which of the three points — A, B, or C — should White play? Consider the strength and weakness of the two white positions on the left and right.

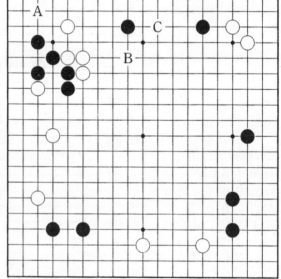

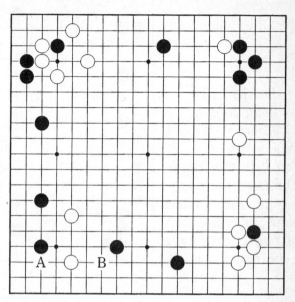

Problem 121.
Black to play.

A or B: which point should Black play? Bear in mind that the white position on the right is extremely strong.

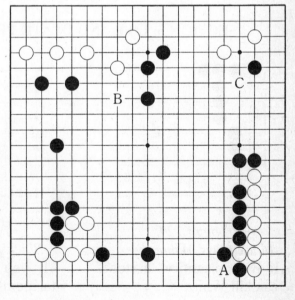

Problem 122.
White to play.

The next move is very important since it will determine the direction of the middle game. Of the three points A, B, and C, which one should White play?

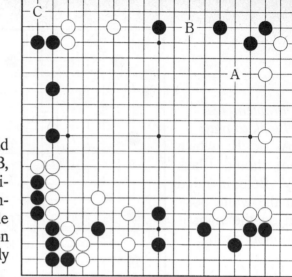

Problem 123.
White to play.
Where should White play — A, B, or C? In the transition from the opening to the middle game, the direction of play is extremely important.

SECTION 3. LIFE AND DEATH PROBLEMS

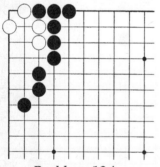

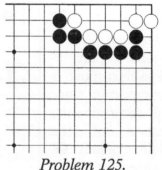

Problem 124.
Black plays, White dies.
If Black sacrifices a stone, he can kill White.

Problem 125.
Black plays, White dies.
If you hit White on the vital point, all his stones will die.

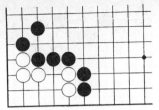

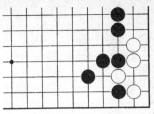

Problem 126.
Black plays, White dies.
Since White's two stones on the right are short of liberties, you can kill the whole group unconditionally.

Problem 127.
Black plays, White dies.
The first move is the most important.

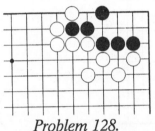

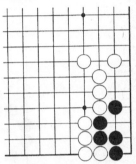

Problem 128.
White plays, Black dies.
"There's death in the hane," is a famous proverb. But in order to kill Black, a good follow-up is necessary.

Problem 129.
White to play and get a ko.
Whether Black lives or dies depends on a ko.

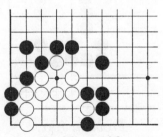

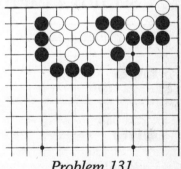

Problem 130.
White to play and get a ko.
Turn this position into a ko.

Problem 131.
White to play and live.
If White can sacrifice the three stones in the corner, he can get a second eye.

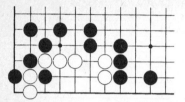

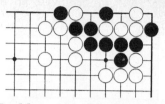

Problem 132. Black to play.
White lives or dies depending on how he captures the lone black stone.

Problem 133. Black to play.
Because of a special situation known as "long life", Black can live. How does Black manage it?

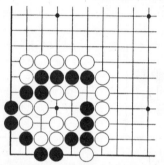

Problem 134. Black plays and lives.
This is a strange position, but with the right move, Black can live.

SECTION 4. CAPTURING-RACE PROBLEMS

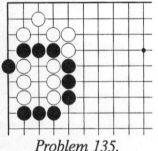

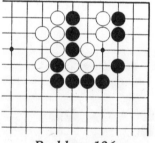

Problem 135.
Black to play and win.
Black has to capture three white stones and rescue three of his own.

Problem 136.
Black to play and win.
Black to rescue his three stones and capture three of White's.

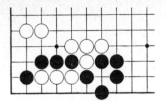

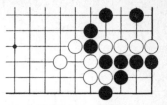

Problem 137.
White to play and win.
White can capture the four black stones in the corner.

Problem 138.
Black to play and win.
Capture the four white stones. Ko is a failure.

SECTION 5. ENDGAME PROBLEMS

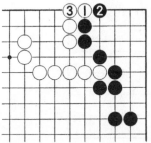

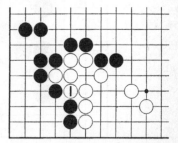

Problem 139. Black to play.
How should Black answer White 3? A mistake could cost Black two points.

Problem 140. Black to play.
How should Black answer White 1? A mistake here could cost Black four points.

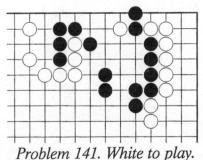

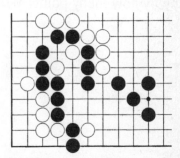

Problem 141. White to play.
Reduce Black's territory as much as possible. The first move is the most important.

Problem 142. White to play.
What is the move to devastate Black's territory here?

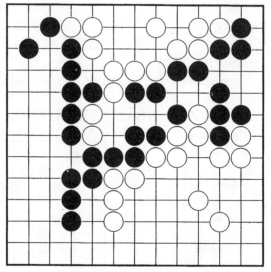

Problem 143. White to play.

This problem comes from a game on a 13x13 board.

1. What is White's biggest endgame move?

2. Play out the rest of the game with the best moves and determine by how many points White wins.

ADVANCED PROBLEMS
LEVEL THREE

LIFE AND DEATH
PROBLEMS

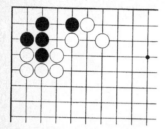

Problem 144 (1 move)
Black to play and live.
Make the move which will expand Black's territory as much as possible.

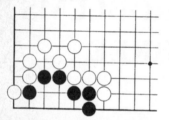

Problem 146 (1 move)
Black to play and live.
Beware of a ko.

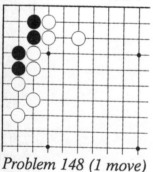

Problem 148 (1 move)
Black to play and live.
You have to play on the vital point.

Problem 145 (1 move)
Black to play and live.
Black has to make an open connection, but on which side?

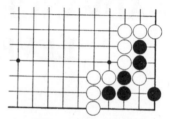

Problem 147 (1 move)
Black to play and live.
Make the move which will expand Black's territory as much as possible.

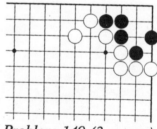

Problem 149 (3 moves)
Black to play and live.
You have to play on the vital point.

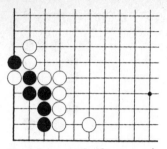

Problem 150 (3 moves)
Black to play and live.
The black stone that is in atari is crucial to this problem.

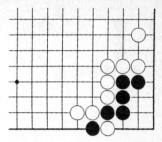

Problem 151 (3 moves)
Black to play and live.
The black stone that is in atari is crucial to this problem.

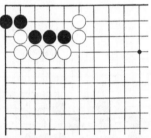

Problem 152 (1 move)
Black to play and live.
You have to play on the vital point.

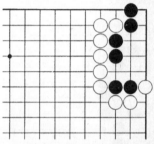

Problem 153 (1 move)
Black to play and live.
Take into account the two black stones which are short of liberties.

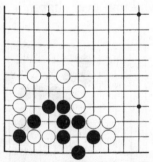

Problem 154 (1 move)
Black to play and live.
If Black can capture the two white stones, he lives.

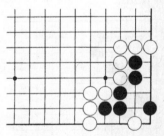

Problem 155 (1 move)
Black to play and live.
Black has two ways to live. What are they?

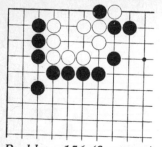

Problem 156 (3 moves)
White to play and live.
The white stone that is in atari is crucial to this problem.

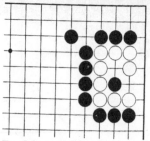

Problem 157 (3 moves)
White to play and live.
Play for a seki.

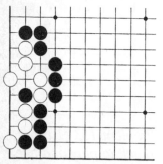

Problem 158 (3 moves)
White to play and live.
You have to play on the vital point.

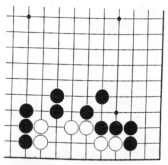

Problem 159 (3 moves)
White to play and live.
Making eye shape is crucial.

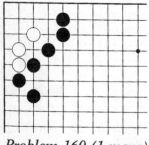

Problem 160 (1 move)
White to play and live.
Play on the vital point.

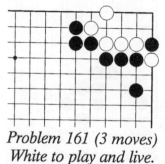

Problem 161 (3 moves)
White to play and live.
There are three ways for White to live. What are they?

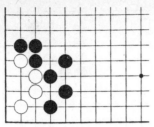

Problem 162 (1 move)
White to play and live.
Getting a ko is not good enough.

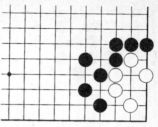

Problem 163 (3 moves)
White to play and live.
White has a lot of liberties, so he can live.

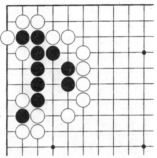

Problem 164 (3 moves)
Black to play and live.
The only way to live is to capture a white stone.

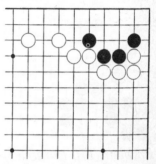

Problem 165 (1 move)
Black to play and live.
The obvious move doesn't work.

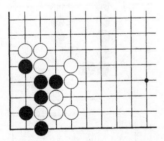

Problem 166 (1 move)
Black to play and live.
Getting a ko is not good enough.

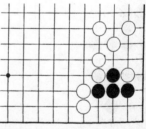

Problem 167 (3 moves)
Black to play and live.
Capturing a stone right away fails. Play the vital points.

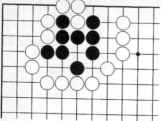

Problem 168 (5 moves)
Black to play and live.
You have to capture three white stones.

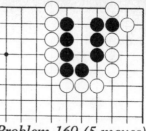

Problem 169 (5 moves)
Black to play and live.
Black can live because the corner is nearby.

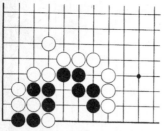

Problem 170 (3 moves)
Black to play and live.
The two black stones that are in atari are crucial to this problem.

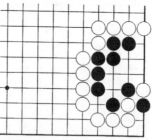

Problem 171 (3 moves)
Black to play and live.
The black stone that is in atari is crucial to this problem.

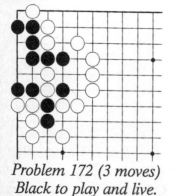

Problem 172 (3 moves)
Black to play and live.
Capturing the two white stones is not your first priority.

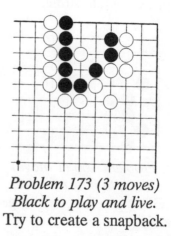

Problem 173 (3 moves)
Black to play and live.
Try to create a snapback.

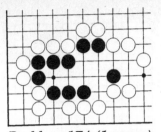

Problem 174 (1 move)
Black to play and live.

Make the move which will expand Black's territory as much as possible.

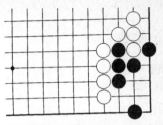

Problem 175 (1 move)
Black to play and live.

A move on the vital point secures life.

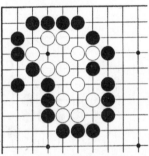

Problem 176 (1 move)
White to play and live.

White seems to have secured two eyes, but one more move is needed.

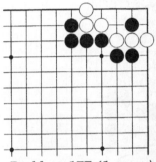

Problem 177 (1 move)
White to play and live.

Beware of a ko.

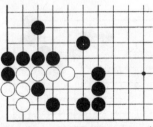

Problem 178 (7 moves)
White to play and live.

Threaten to sacrifice a stone.

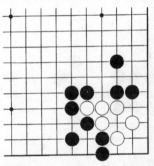

Problem 179 (3 moves)
White to play and live.

You have to think about Black's stone on the first line.

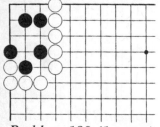

Problem 180 (1 move)
Black to play and live.

Black seems to have enough eyes, but the next move is crucial.

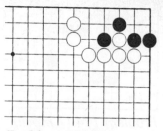

Problem 181 (3 moves)
Black to play and live.

The black stone on the left is crucial if Black is to live.

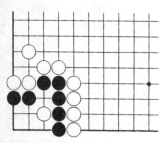

Problem 182 (1 move)
Black to play and live.

Beware of a ko.

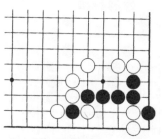

Problem 183 (5 moves)
Black to play and live.

You have to pay special attention to the two white stones in the corner.

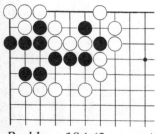

Problem 184 (3 moves)
Black to play and live.

Capture the four white stones in the corner.

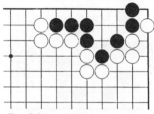

Problem 185 (3 moves)
Black to play and live.

The black stone in atari is not important.

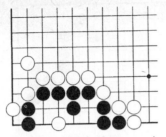

Problem 186 (3 moves)
Black to play and live.
What is the most profitable
way to live.

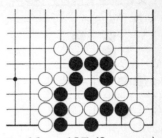

Problem 187 (3 moves)
Black to play and live.
If you know the under-the-
stones tesuji, you can live.

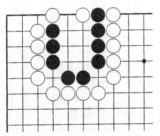

Problem 188 (5 moves)
Black to play and live.
Black has to sacrifice a
stone to live.

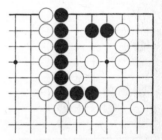

Problem 189 (5 moves)
Black to play and live.
Black has to sacrifice a
stone to live.

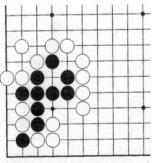

Problem 190 (3 moves)
Black to play and live.
The problem is how to cap-
ture the two white stones.

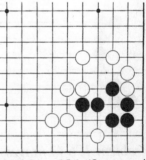

Problem 191 (9 moves)
Black to play and live.
Black has to sacrifice a
stone to live.

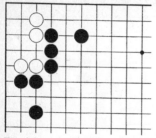

Problem 192 (3 moves)
Black plays, White dies.
Reduce the liberties of the lower two white stones.

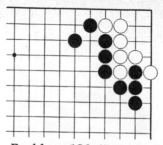

Problem 193 (5 moves)
Black plays, White dies.
Don't let White's stone on the first line come into play.

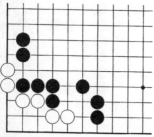

Problem 194 (5 moves)
Black plays, White dies.
Create a 4-point nakade in the corner.

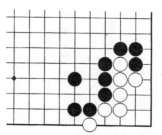

Problem 195 (5 moves)
Black plays, White dies.
There are two ways to kill White. What are they?

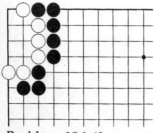

Problem 196 (3 moves)
Black plays, White dies.
Don't play for a ko; kill White by creating a 4-point nakade.

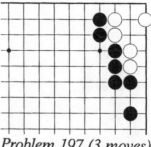

Problem 197 (3 moves)
Black plays, White dies.
There are two vital points, but the order of playing them is not important.

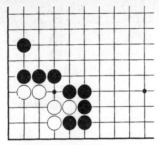

Problem 198 (9 moves)
Black plays, White dies.
Black must aim to make a
5-point nakade.

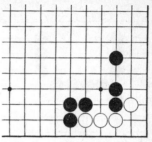

Problem 199 (7 moves)
Black plays, White dies.
Remember, the bent-four-
in-the-corner shape is dead.

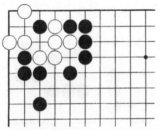

Problem 200 (11 moves)
Black plays, White dies.
Black has to sacrifice six
stones to kill White.

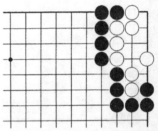

Problem 201 (3 moves)
Black plays, White dies.
Black has to play on the
vital point and then sacrifice a
stone.

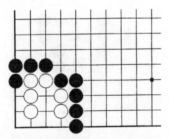

Problem 202 (5 moves)
Black plays, White dies.
The trick here is to create a
shortage of liberties.

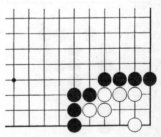

Problem 203 (3 moves)
Black plays, White dies.
Again the trick is to create
a shortage of liberties.

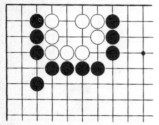

Problem 204 (3 moves)
Black plays, White dies.
Be careful not to let White live in a seki.

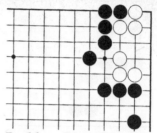

Problem 205 (5 moves)
Black plays, White dies.
Kill White by creating a 5-point nakade.

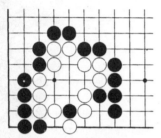

Problem 206 (3 moves)
Black plays, White dies.
Kill White by taking advantage of his shortage of liberties.

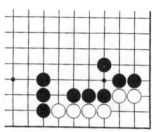

Problem 207 (3 moves)
Black plays, White dies.
Two of White's stones are short of liberties.

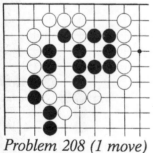

Problem 208 (1 move)
White plays, Black dies.
Consider White's own weak point before attacking.

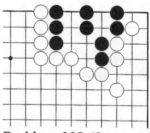

Problem 209 (3 moves)
White plays, Black dies.
Black is short of liberties, so White can easily kill him.

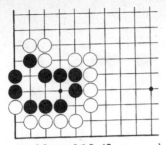

Problem 210 (3 moves)
White plays, Black dies.
The first move is a quiet one.

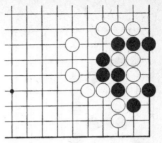

Problem 211 (3 moves)
White plays, Black dies.
Don't let Black get a ko.

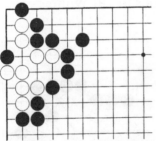

Problem 212 (5 moves)
Black plays, White dies.
First Black must sacrifice two stones, and then one more.

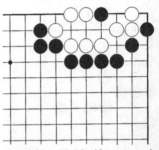

Problem 213 (3 moves)
Black plays, White dies.
After the first move, it will be easy to see that White is dead.

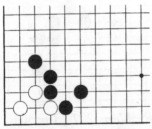

Problem 214 (1 move)
Black plays, White dies.
Don't let White get a ko.

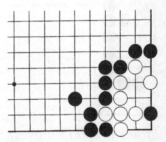

Problem 215 (3 moves)
Black plays, White dies.
Make a bent-four-in-the-corner shape.

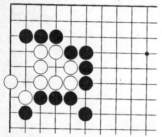

Problem 216 (7 moves)
Black plays, White dies.
Don't let White get a ko.

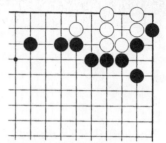

Problem 217 (9 moves)
Black plays, White dies.
Black has to sacrifice two stones to kill White.

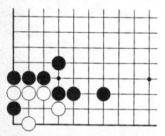

Problem 218 (9 moves)
Black plays, White dies.
Another two-stone sacrifice by Black.

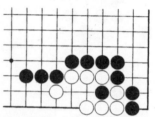

Problem 219 (9 moves)
Black plays, White dies.
This is the same theme as the preceding problem.

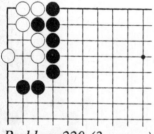

Problem 220 (3 moves)
Black plays, White dies.
Black can kill White because his three stones at the top are short of liberties.

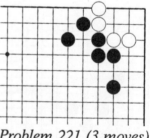

Problem 221 (3 moves)
Black plays, White dies.
If you play on the vital point of White's shape, you can kill him.

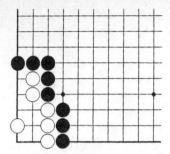

Problem 222 (3 moves)
Black plays, White dies.
Black can kill White by sacrificing a stone.

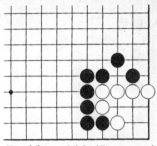

Problem 223 (5 moves)
Black plays, White dies.
Find the vital point in the corner.

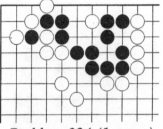

Problem 224 (1 move)
White plays, Black dies.
Utilize the shortage of liberties of Black's three stones on the left.

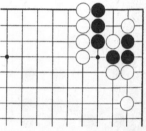

Problem 225 (5 moves)
White plays, Black dies.
"One eye beats no eyes!" Utilizing this proverb will enable you to kill Black.

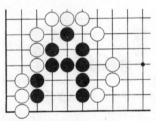

Problem 226 (1 move)
White plays, Black dies.
Because of the stone on the 1–2 point, the black group is dead.

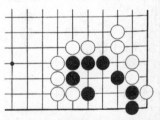

Problem 227 (3 moves)
White plays, Black dies.
After the first move, it will be clear that Black is dead.

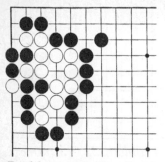

Problem 228 (3 moves)
Black plays, White dies.
The key is how to sacrifice the three black stones.

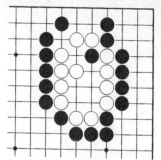

Problem 229 (5 moves)
Black plays, White dies.
Utilize White's shortage of liberties.

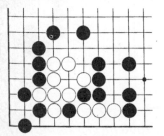

Problem 230 (7 moves)
Black plays, White dies.
A sacrifice is the key to this problem.

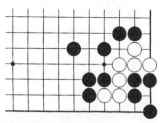

Problem 231 (3 moves)
Black plays, White dies.
Create a 5-point nakade to kill White.

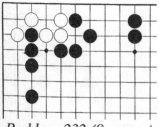

Problem 232 (9 moves)
Black plays, White dies.
Play on the vital point and then make the bent-four-in-the-corner shape.

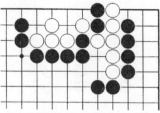

Problem 233 (3 moves)
Black plays, White dies.
Attack White's four stones that are short of liberties.

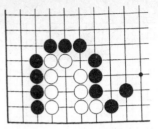

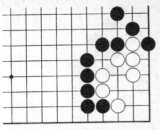

Problem 234 (1 move)
Black plays, White dies.
Don't let White get a seki.

Problem 235 (7 moves)
Black plays, White dies.
Black must choose the
right point of attack.

SECTION 2: KO PROBLEMS

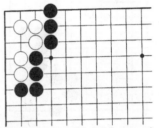

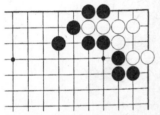

Problem 236 (6 moves)
Black plays and gets a ko.
Black's stones on the first
line enable him to turn the
corner into a ko.

Problem 237 (5 moves)
Black plays and gets a ko.
Black can get a ko because
the five white stones are short
of liberties.

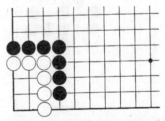

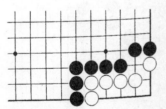

Problem 238 (5 moves)
Black plays and gets a ko.
There are two vital points,
but only one of them is right.

Problem 239 (4 moves)
Black plays and gets a ko.
This becomes an approach-
move ko.

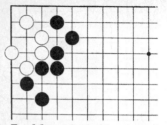

Problem 240 (6 moves)
Black plays and gets a ko.
Because White's two stones have two outside liberties, all Black can get is a ko.

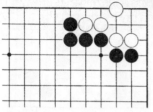

Problem 241 (6 moves)
Black plays and gets a ko.
Find the vital point.

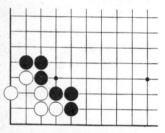

Problem 242 (7 moves)
Black plays and gets a ko.
Because of White's shortage of liberties, Black can get a ko.

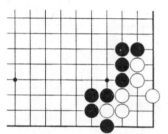

Problem 243 (6 moves)
Black plays and gets a ko.
Because White's three stones are short of liberties, Black can get a ko.

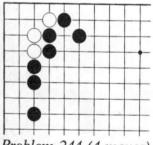

Problem 244 (4 moves)
White plays and gets a ko.
White can't live unconditionally.

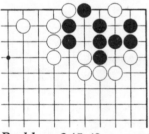

Problem 245 (3 moves)
White plays and gets a ko.
The corner white stone is the key to getting a ko.

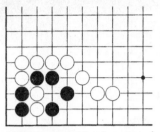

Problem 246 (4 moves)
White plays and gets a ko.
The special character of the corner enables White to get a ko.

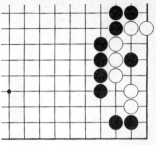

Problem 247 (4 moves)
White plays and gets a ko.
The only way White can live is to get a ko.

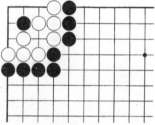

Problem 248 (1 move)
Black plays and gets a ko.
A seki is not good enough.

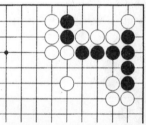

Problem 249 (6 moves)
Black plays and gets a ko.
By utilizing the special character of the corner, Black can get a two-step ko.

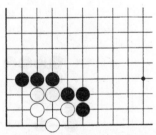

Problem 250 (8 moves)
Black plays and gets a ko.
Black has two ways to get a ko.

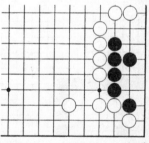

Problem 251 (4 moves)
Black plays and gets a ko.
The only way to live is by ko.

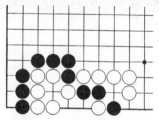

Problem 252 (7 moves)
Black to play and get a ko.
This is not an easy ko to see.

SECTION 3. SEKI PROBLEMS

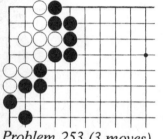

Problem 253 (3 moves)
Black to play and get a seki.
What is the most profitable
way to get a seki?

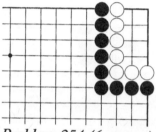

Problem 254 (6 moves)
Black to play and get a seki.
There are two ways to get a
seki. Which is better?

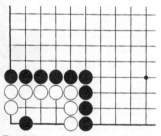

Problem 255 (4 moves)
Black to play and get a seki.
There are two ways to get
seki. Which is better?

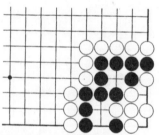

Problem 256 (3 moves)
Black to play and get a seki.
Don't let White turn this
into a real ko!

SECTION 4. CAPTURING RACES

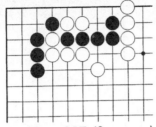

Problem 257 (3 moves)
Black to play and win.
Black has more liberties than White, but he must be careful.

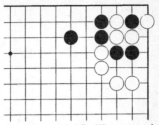

Problem 258 (7 moves)
Black to play and win.
Black has to sacrifice two stones.

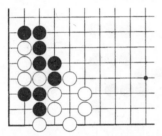

Problem 259 (5 moves)
Black to play and win.
Black fails if it becomes a ko.

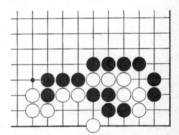

Problem 260 (7 moves)
Black to play and win.
The first move may be hard to see.

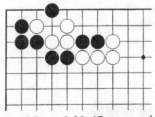

Problem 261 (5 moves)
Black to play and win.
There's only one move that works.

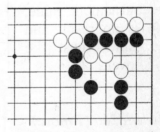

Problem 262 (3 moves)
Black to play and win.
The winning move is a common tesuji.

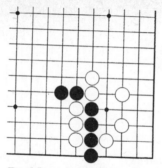

Problem 263 (7 moves)
Black to play and win.
The three white stones cannot escape.

SECTION 5. STRANGE POSITIONS

Problem 264 (1 move)
Black to play and
get a seki.
This position is
known as *hane-seki*.

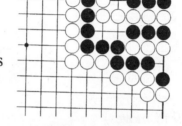

Problem 265 (1 move)
Black to play and
get a triple ko.
If a triple ko occurs
in a tournament game,
there is no result and
the game must be
played over.

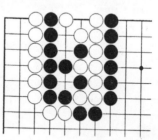

Problem 266 (1 move)
Black plays, White dies.
In spite of a double
ko, White dies.

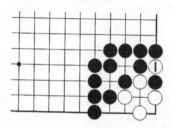

ADVANCED PROBLEMS
LEVEL FOUR

LIFE AND DEATH
PROBLEMS

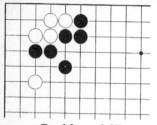

Problem 267
Black plays, White dies.
First, play a quiet move.

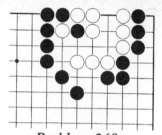

Problem 268
Black plays, White dies.
The solution involves a shortage of liberties.

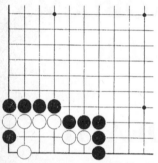

Problem 269
Black plays, White dies.
The key to killing White lies in the isolated black stone in the corner.

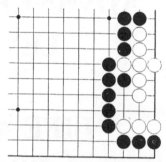

Problem 270
Black plays, White dies.
The solution involves a shortage of liberties.

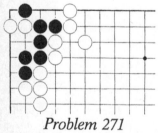

Problem 271
Black to play and live.
Don't let White turn this into a ko.

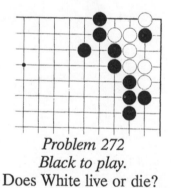

Problem 272
Black to play.
Does White live or die?

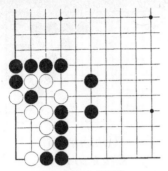

Problem 273
Black plays, White dies.
Don't let this become a ko.

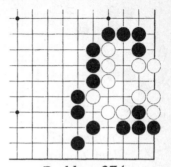

Problem 274
Black plays, White dies.
Hit White on the vital point.

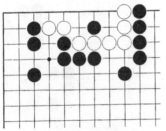

Problem 275
White to play and live.
White must try to get a seki.

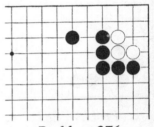

Problem 276
White to play and live.
First and foremost, White must think about eye shape.

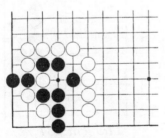

Problem 277
White plays, Black dies.
Create a 5-point nakade.

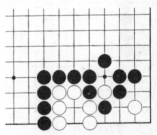

Problem 278
White to play and live.
Don't let Black turn this into a ko.

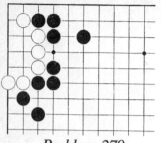

Problem 279
Black to play.

Black can turn this into a ko.

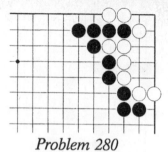

Problem 280
Black to play.

Since White is short of liberties, Black can turn this into a ko.

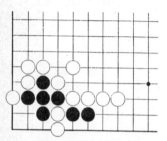

Problem 281
Black to play.

Aim to live with just the four stones in the corner.

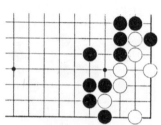

Problem 282
Black plays, White dies.

Play on the vital point of the corner.

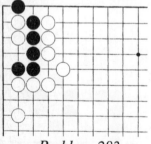

Problem 283
Black to play and live.

Since Black's group has a liberty, he can live in seki.

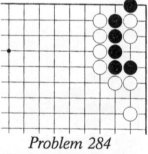

Problem 284
Black to play and live.

The liberty is gone in this position, so the best Black can do is to live with a ko.

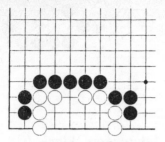

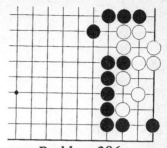

Problem 285
Black plays, White dies.
Kill White by creating a 5-point nakade.

Problem 286
Black plays, White dies.
The first move is important.

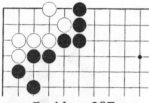

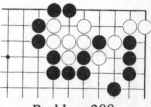

Problem 287
Black plays, White dies.
First sacrifice a stone and then make a bent-four-in-the-corner.

Problem 288
Black plays, White dies.
Create a shortage of liberties with the six white stones on the left.

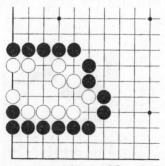

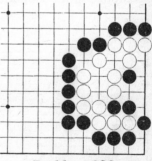

Problem 289
Black plays, White dies.
Aim at creating a 4-point nakade.

Problem 290
Black plays, White dies.
Since White's four stones at the top are short of liberties, all his stones will die.

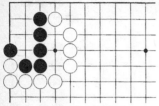

Problem 291
White plays, Black dies.
Finding the first move is important.

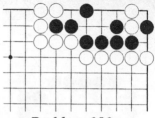

Problem 292
White plays, Black dies.
First of all, White has to sacrifice a stone.

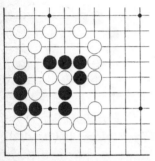

Problem 293
White plays, Black dies.
Create a 5-point nakade.

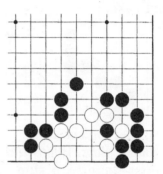

Problem 294
White to play and live.
Sacrifice the stone that's in atari.

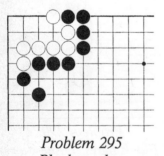

Problem 295
Black to play.
Best play for both sides results in a ko.

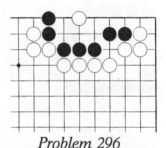

Problem 296
Black to play and live.
Squeeze the breath out of White.

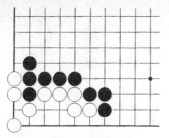

Problem 297
Black plays, White dies.
Put the whole white group into a shortage of liberties.

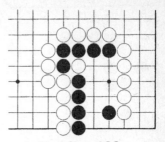

Problem 298
Black to play and live.
You have to capture the white stone correctly.

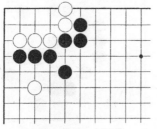

Problem 299
Black to play.
White cannot live unconditionally.

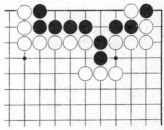

Problem 300
Black to play and live.
Utilize the black stone in atari.

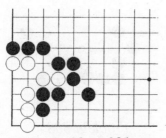

Problem 301
Black plays, White dies.
Note that White has two stones short of liberties.

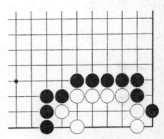

Problem 302
Black plays, White dies.
Attack at the vital point

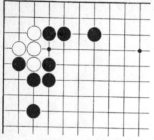

Problem 303
Black plays, White dies.

First, you have to attack the vital point.

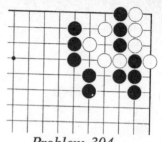

Problem 304
Black plays, White dies.

Stop White from getting two eyes.

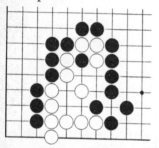

Problem 305
Black plays, White dies.

Capturing only three stones is not good enough.

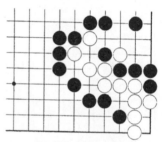

Problem 306
Black plays, White dies.

You have to find the right way to rescue the four black stones on the right.

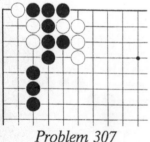

Problem 307
White to play and live.

You have to find the right way to prevent Black from cutting in the corner.

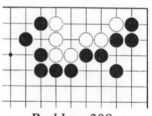

Problem 308
White to play and live.

You have to find the right way to prevent Black from capturing.

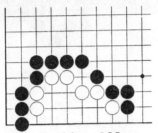

Problem 309
White to play and live.
White has to play the proper 'shape' move.

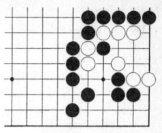

Problem 310
White to play and live.
White has to sacrifice two stones.

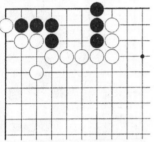

Problem 311
Black to play and live.
You have to find the vital point for making two eyes.

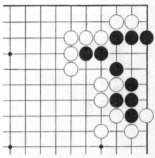

Problem 312
Black to play and live.
You have to find the vital point for making two eyes.

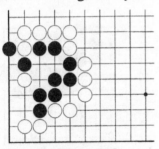

Problem 313
Black to play and live.
How does Black capture the isolated white stone?

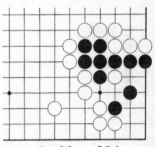

Problem 314
Black to play and live.
The correct move is not obvious.

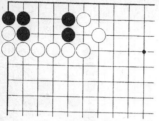

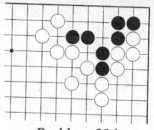

Problem 315
Black to play and live.
Don't let White make a nakade.

Problem 316
Black to play and live.
If you find the vital point, living will be easy.

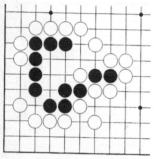

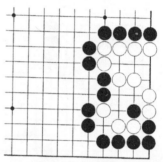

Problem 317
Black to play and live.
The key is how to sacrifice the two black stones.

Problem 318
Black plays, White dies.
The order of moves is important here.

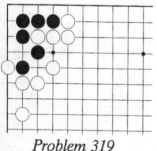

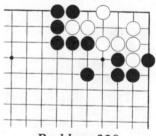

Problem 319
Black to play.
Black cannot live unconditionally.

Problem 320
Black plays, White dies.
The two white stones on the left are short of liberties.

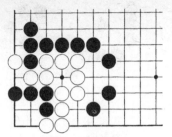

Problem 321
Black plays, White dies.
Don't let White make an eye in the corner.

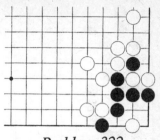

Problem 322
Black to play and live.
Black's group can live because of the liberty on the outside.

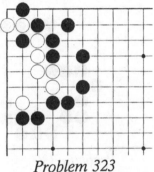

Problem 323
White to play and live.
White has to sacrifice two stones to live.

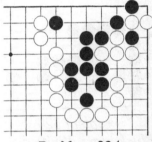

Problem 324
White plays, Black dies.
Don't let Black get a ko.

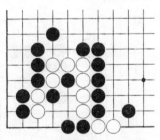

Problem 325
White to play and live.
You have to capture all the black stones at the same time.

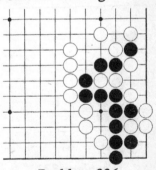

Problem 326
White plays, Black dies.
You have to find the best way to sacrifice the two white stones.

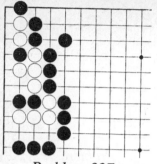

Problem 327
Black plays, White dies.
Kill White by creating a shortage of liberties.

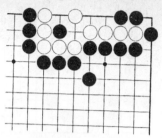

Problem 328
Black plays, White dies.
You have to make two successive sacrifices.

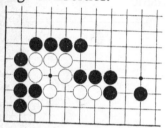

Problem 329
Black plays, White dies.
First play on the vital point, then rescue that stone.

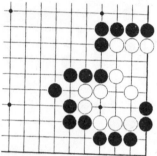

Problem 330
Black plays, White dies.
The order of moves is important in creating a shortage of liberties.

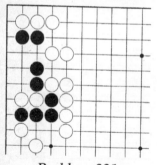

Problem 331
Black to play and live.
The key to this problem is how to capture the two white stones.

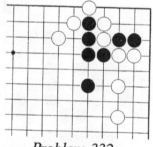

Problem 332
Black to play and live.
There's a way to rescue the two black stones in the corner.

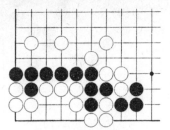

Problem 333
Black to play and live.
Black can save his stones
by capturing three white ones.

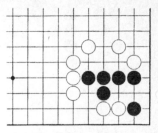

Problem 334
Black to play and live.
Black has to sacrifice a
stone to make eyes for his
group in the corner.

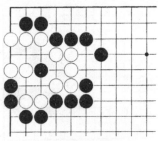

Problem 335
Black plays, White dies.
Where's the vital point?

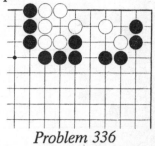

Problem 336
Black plays, White dies.
You can kill White by
sacrificing two stones.

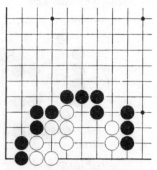

Problem 337
Black plays, White dies.
Play on the vital point.

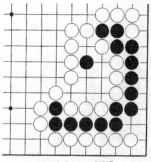

Problem 338
Black to play and live.
If Black captures three
white stones, he can live.

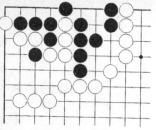

Problem 339
White plays, Black dies.
In order to kill Black, you have to sacrifice two stones.

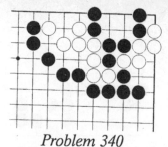

Problem 340
White to play and live.
White has to sacrifice the five stones on the right if his other stones are to live.

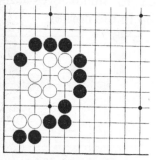

Problem 341
White to play and live.
White has to make one more eye.

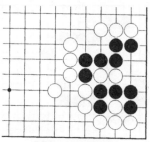

Problem 342
White plays, Black dies.
How to sacrifice the two white stones is the key.

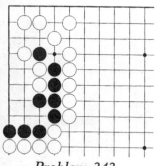

Problem 343
Black to play and live.
Black has to sacrifice a stone in order to live.

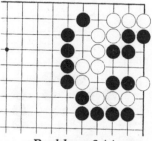

Problem 344
Black plays, White dies.
Don't let this situation become a seki. Kill all the white stones.

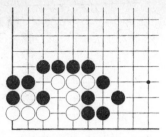

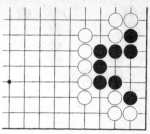

Problem 345
Black plays, White dies.
Make the five white stones short of liberties.

Problem 346
Black to play and live.
The order of moves is important.

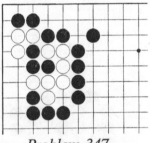

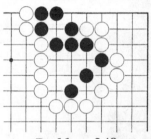

Problem 347
Black plays, White dies.
Think about the shape after the three black stones are captured.

Problem 348
Black to play and live.
If you don't approach this problem thoughtlessly, you can expect Black to live.

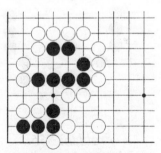

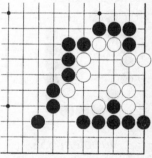

Problem 349
Black to play and live.
Black has to sacrifice a stone to live.

Problem 350
Black plays, White dies.
You have to make White short of liberties.

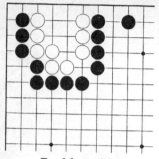

Problem 351
Black plays, White dies.
You have to decide on which side to hane.

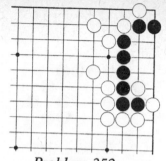

Problem 352
Black to play and live.
Black has to sacrifice a stone in order to live.

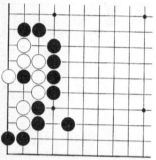

Problem 353
Black plays, White dies.
How should Black sacrifice the stone in atari.

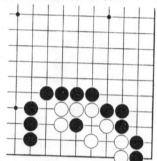

Problem 354
Black plays, White dies.
Attack the two white stones that are short of liberties.

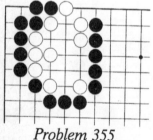

Problem 355
White to play and live.
Make a move with two threats.

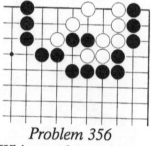

Problem 356
White to play and live.
If you try to capture the two black stones too quickly, you will fail.

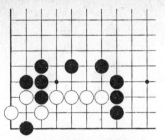

Problem 357
White to play and live.
White has to give up two of his corner stones.

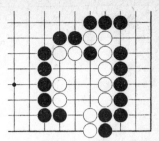

Problem 358
White to play and live.
Give up the two stones on the edge.

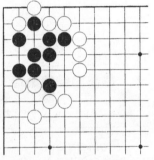

Problem 359
Black plays and gets a ko.
The only way Black can live is with a ko.

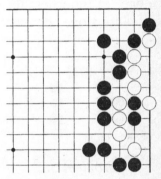

Problem 360
Black plays, White dies.
Don't let this position become a ko.

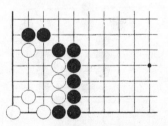

Problem 361
Black plays, White dies.
If you play on the vital point, you can capture all the white stones.

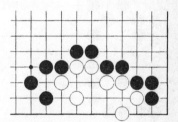

Problem 362
Black plays, White dies.
The order of moves is important.

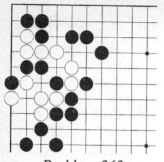

Problem 363
Black plays, White dies.
You have to create a shortage of liberties for the three white stones below.

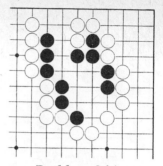

Problem 364
Black to play and live.
Play on the vital point for making eye shape.

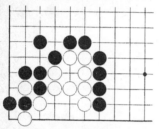

Problem 365
Black plays, White dies.
Make White short of liberties.

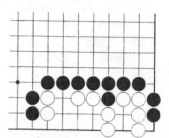

Problem 366
Black plays, White dies.
Make White's two stones on the left short of liberties.

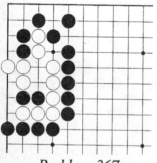

Problem 367
Black plays, White dies.
Create a shortage of liberties.

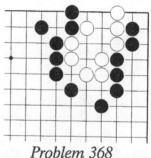

Problem 368
Black plays, White dies.
Utilize Black's stone on the first line.

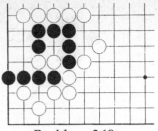

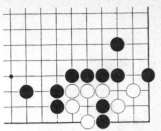

Problem 369
Black to play and live.
Black has to be satisfied with a seki.

Problem 370
Black plays, White dies.
You can kill White by making him short of liberties.

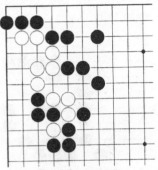

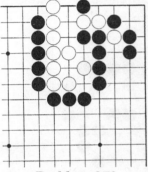

Problem 371
White to play and live.
Utilize Black's shortage of liberties.

Problem 372
White to play and live.
White can live because of his stone in atari.

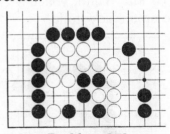

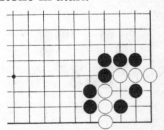

Problem 373
White to play and live.
The correct order of moves enables you to capture some black stones and get two eyes.

Problem 374
White to play and live.
Be careful not to let Black turn the corner into a nakade.

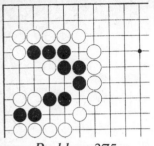

Problem 375
Black to play and live.
You must find the right way to capture the lone white stone.

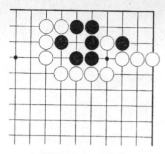

Problem 376
Black to play and live.
You have to utilize the black stone in the corner in the right way.

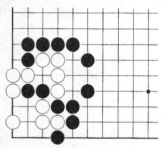

Problem 377
Black plays, White dies.
Create a shortage of liberties in the corner.

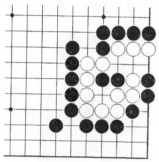

Problem 378
Black plays, White dies.
To kill White, you have to give up a black stone.

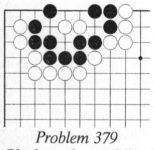

Problem 379
Black to play and live.
Don't let White make a nakade; turn this into a seki.

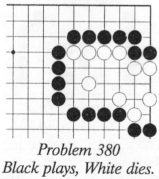

Problem 380
Black plays, White dies.
Strike at the vital point.

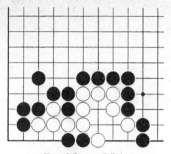

Problem 381
Black plays and gets a ko.
Make White short of liberties.

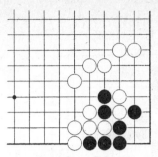

Problem 382
Black to play and live.
Black has to give up two stones in the center to make his others live.

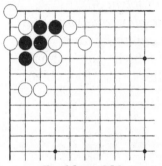

Problem 383
Black to play and live.
Black can create a double ko and live.

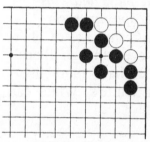

Problem 384
Black plays, White dies.
Black kills White with a double ko.

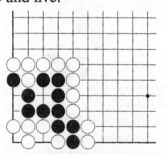

Problem 385
Black to play and live.
Black makes a double ko and wins the capturing race.

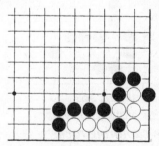

Problem 386
Black plays and gets a ko.
Black creates an approach-move ko.

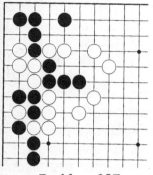

Problem 387
*White plays and wins
the capturing race.*

Create a shortage of liberties and even though Black's four stones have more liberties than White's, White can still win.

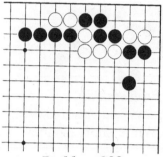

Problem 388
*White plays and wins
the capturing race.*

From which side should White attack the four black stones?

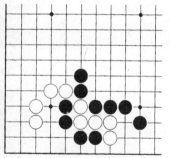

Problem 389
*White plays and wins
the capturing race.*

White has to sacrifice two stones.

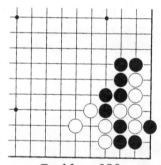

Problem 390
*White plays and wins
the capturing race.*

White will succeed if he can get a ko.

ANSWERS

PROBLEM 1

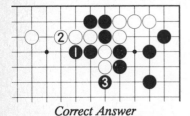

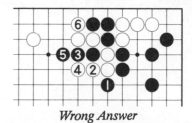

Correct Answer

When Black plays 1, the points 2 and 3 become *miai*, so Black can capture some white stones in a ladder.

Wrong Answer

Playing *atari* with 1 first fails. Black must answer 4 with 5, after which White plays 6. The three black stones at the top will be captured.

PROBLEM 2

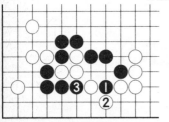

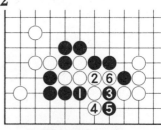

Correct Answer

Black 1 is the *tesuji*. If White answers with 2, Black catches three white stones by playing 3.

Wrong Answer

If Black plays 1 without any preparation, White plays the moves to 6, and Black has no follow-up.

PROBLEM 3

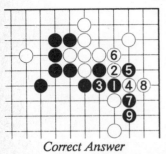

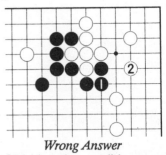

Correct Answer

The open connection of Black 1 is correct. With the moves up to Black 9, White's two groups have been effectively separated.

Wrong Answer

If Black makes a solid connection at 1, White plays 2 and his stones on the right side are linked up. Black has failed.

PROBLEM 4

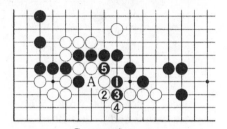

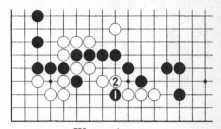

Correct Answer

Black 1 is the *tesuji*. If White resists with 2 and 4, after Black 5, White must give up his two stones in *atari*. If White 2 at 3, Black A.

Wrong Answer

Black 1 may look like a *tesuji*, but after White 2, Black has no effective continuation.

PROBLEM 5

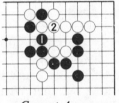

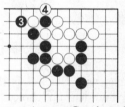

Correct Answer

It is correct to atari first with 1. White is forced to connect with 2, after which —

Correct Answer Continuation

Black ataris with 3. This is the correct order of moves.

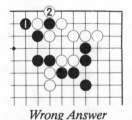

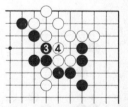

Wrong Answer

If Black first ataris with 1, of course White captures with 2.

Wrong Answer Continuation

If Black now plays 3, White answers with 4, so Black's three stones are short of liberties. This result is inferior to the correct answer.

PROBLEM 6

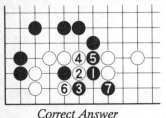

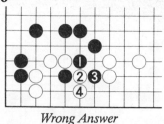

Correct Answer

Black should jump down and attach at 1. If White resists with 2, the moves to 7 follow. White has been separated into two groups.

Wrong Answer

Black 1 does not work. White answers with 2 and 4, and Black has run out of moves. The white position is still intact as one group.

PROBLEM 7

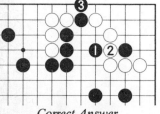

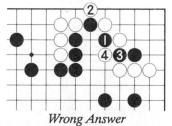

Correct Answer

Peeping with Black 1 is the key move. White has no choice but to defend at 2 and limit his loss. Black can now isolate the four white stones at the top with 3.

Wrong Answer

Black 1 fails. Black may try 3 in response to 2, but after White 4 he has no follow-up.

PROBLEM 8

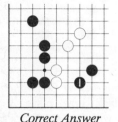

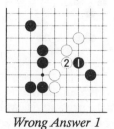

Correct Answer

Black 1 destroys the base of White's group while making good shape for his stones on the right.

Wrong Answer 1

Black 1 here may attack the white stones, but the black stones are heavy and make an inefficient shape.

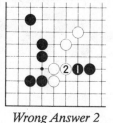

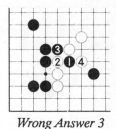

Wrong Answer 2

Black 1 is too direct. After White 2, Black's stones on the right are heavy and vulnerable to attack.

Wrong Answer 3

Trying to separate the stones below from the ones at the top with 1 and 3 fails after White plays 4. Clearly, Black 1 in the correct answer is best, since it gives Black good shape.

PROBLEM 9

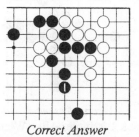

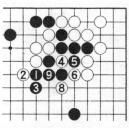

Correct Answer

Extending to 1 is the move that prevents Black's shape from collapsing.

Wrong Answer

7: connects at 4

If Black tries to attack White's stones with 1, White exchanges 2 for 3, then turns Black's group into a shapeless clump of stones up to 8.

PROBLEM 10

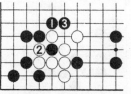

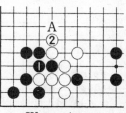

Correct Answer

The stone in atari is not important. Black *ataris* with 1 and continues to attack White's group with 3.

Wrong Answer

If Black rescues his stone with 1, White plays either 2 or A and he will have no problem with these stones.

PROBLEM 11

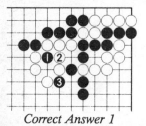

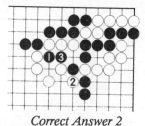

Correct Answer 1

Black should cut at 1. If White answers with 2, Black plays 3 and is connected to the outside. White can't cut off the seven black stones because he is short of liberties.

Correct Answer 2

If White cuts from the outside with 2, Black plays 3, capturing three white stones.

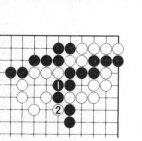

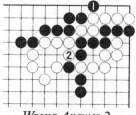

Wrong Answer 1

If Black simply connects at 1, White cuts with 2, so the black stones will die.

Wrong Answer 2

Black 1 is futile. After White 2, it is clear that Black cannot win the capturing race.

PROBLEM 12

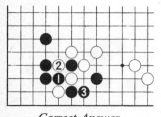

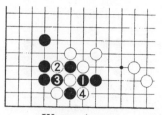

Correct Answer

Black 1 enables Black to link up without any problems.

Wrong Answer

If Black plays from the other side, White gets a *ko* by playing 2 and 4.

PROBLEM 13

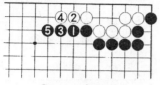

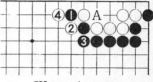

Correct Answer

Extending to 1 is correct. If White keeps pushing along the second line, it is to Black's advantage to keep extending with 3 and 5.

Wrong Answer

Trying to confine White to the corner with 1 is unreasonable. White easily breaks out with 2 and 4. Note that now a move at A is not a threat.

PROBLEM 14

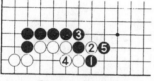

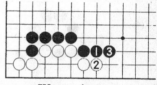

Correct Answer

Black 1 is correct. White must come back and connect at 4. Finally, Black catches the stone at 2 in a ladder, confining White to the corner.

Wrong Answer

In this position, extending with 1 and 3 is passive. Black has failed to take full advantage of White's weak position.

PROBLEM 15

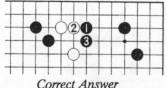

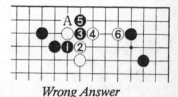

Correct Answer

Extending to 1 robs White of his base and increases Black's territory at the same time.

Wrong Answer

The sequence to 5 enables Black to capture a stones, but White 6 puts Black in a dilemma. He must either capture a stone with A and lose his advantage in the corner, or defend the corner and lose two of his own stones when White plays at A.

PROBLEM 16

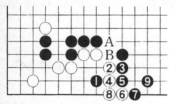

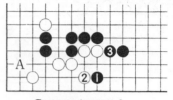

Correct Answer 1

Black 1 is the vital point. Even though White can capture this stone, White is confined to the left side. Later Black can play A or B in *sente*.

Correct Answer 2

If White answers 1 with 2, Black plays 3, again confining White to the left. Later Black can threaten the life of the white stones with A.

PROBLEM 17

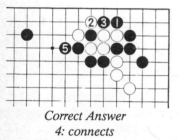

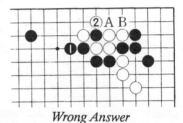

Correct Answer
4: connects

The *ataris* of Black 1 and 3, followed by 5, kill the white stones. White 2 at 3 leads to an immediate capture.

Wrong Answer

If Black plays 1, White is alive after capturing at 2. If Black 1 at A, White B, and Black must go back to defend the stones on the outside, letting White easily get two eyes.

PROBLEM 18

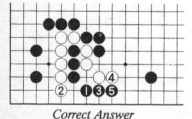

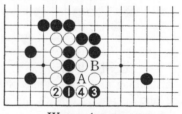

Correct Answer

The diagonal move of 1 enables Black to link up with his stone on the right. If 2 at 3, Black plays 2 and links up with the stones on the left.

Wrong Answer

Black 1 enables White to capture four stones with 2 and 4. If Black plays 1 at A, White responds with B, so the black stones cannot escape.

PROBLEM 19

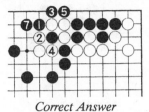

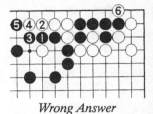

Correct Answer

Black squeezes White with 1, 3 and 5, then draws back with 7. The white stones have no way to escape.

Wrong Answer

If Black saves one stone with the moves to 5, he loses the six on the right after White plays 6.

PROBLEM 20

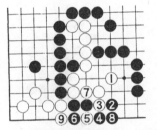

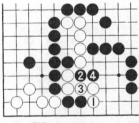

Correct Answer

White 1 is the move that saves all his stones. After 9, if Black plays at 5, he loses all his stones on the edge.

Wrong Answer

White 1 captures two stones at the bottom, but he loses five of his stones above.

PROBLEM 21

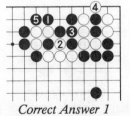

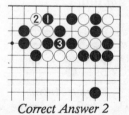

Correct Answer 1

Black should atari with 1. If White captures with 2, Black plays 3 and 5, connecting with good shape.

Correct Answer 2

If White resists with 2, Black connects with 3, so White loses four stones at the top.

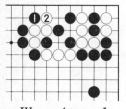
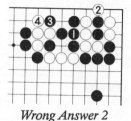

Wrong Answer 1

Black 1 here ends with the loss of Black's four stones after White plays 2.

Wrong Answer 2

If Black first ataris with 1 and then plays 3, White will play 4 and Black now loses his stones at the top.

PROBLEM 22

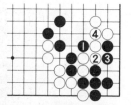
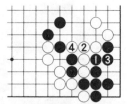

Correct Answer

Black 1 and 3 enable Black to live in the corner with sente.

Wrong Answer

If Black ataris from the other direction, he lives with 3, but White can capture two stones with 4.

PROBLEM 23

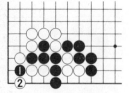
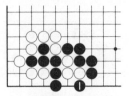

Correct Answer

Black sacrifices a stone with 1. White must answer at 2, and Black plays elsewhere; he can now capture the white stones any time he wants.

Correct Answer

If Black directly captures with 1, White will play elsewhere, so Black has lost sente.

PROBLEM 24

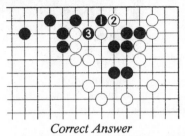

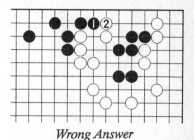

Correct Answer
After Black 1 and 3, there is no way that White can prevent Black from linking up.

Wrong Answer
If Black plays 1, there is no way for Black to rescue his six stones on the right after White 2.

PROBLEM 25

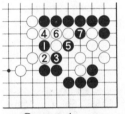

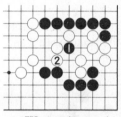

Correct Answer
Black 1, followed by the sequence to 7, is the way that Black captures the six white stones on the right.

Wrong Answer
Black 1 fails, since after 2 White's stones are linked to the outside.

PROBLEM 26

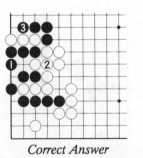

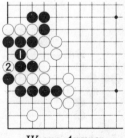

Correct Answer
Black 1 aims to sacrifice two stones, yet his connection on the first line will still be secure.

Wrong Answer
If Black plays 1, he loses his corner stones immediately after White double-ataris at 2.

PROBLEM 27

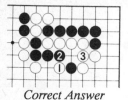

Correct Answer
If Black resists White 1 with 2, connecting at 3 is the key move.

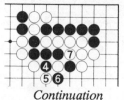

Continuation
Trying to break out with Black 4 and 6 leads to a ladder.

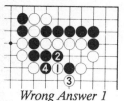

Wrong Answer 1
If White 3, Black easily breaks out into the center with 2 and 4.

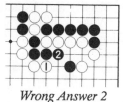

Wrong Answer 2
White 1 also fails. After 2, White can't prevent Black from escaping.

PROBLEM 28

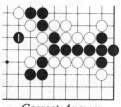

Correct Answer
When Black plays 1, White loses his two key stones.

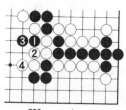

Wrong Answer
Black 1 and 3 let White escape with 2 and 4.

PROBLEM 29

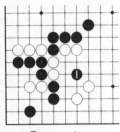

Correct Answer
After 1, White loses the two stones imprisoning the black ones.

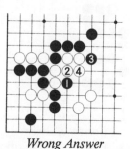

Wrong Answer
Black 1 is a crude move. After White 4, Black has no follow-up.

PROBLEM 30

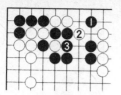

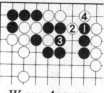

Correct Answer

After 1, White can't stop Black from capturing two stones at the top.

Wrong Answer

Black 1 fails after White links up with 2 and 4.

PROBLEM 31

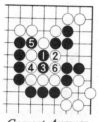

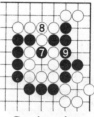

Correct Answer

After Black plays 1, he sacrifices two stones with the sequence to 5. After White captures with 6 —

Continuation

Black throws in a stone with 7. After 9, White can't capture because he is short of liberties.

PROBLEM 32

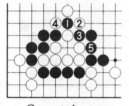

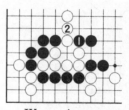

Correct Answer

Black 1 is the key move. Black then captures White up to 5.

Wrong Answer

Exchanging 1 for 2 fails. Black will now lose his four stones below.

PROBLEM 33

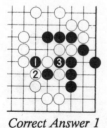

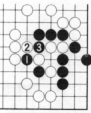

Correct Answer 1

After Black 1, no matter what White does he cannot prevent the capture of his two stones

Correct Answer 2

Blocking from above with White 2 is answered by 3. White can't connect because he is short of liberties.

PROBLEM 34

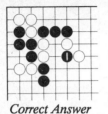

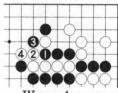

Correct Answer

After Black 1, White has no way to save his two endangered stones.

Wrong Answer

If Black exchanges 1 for 2, White escapes into the center.

PROBLEM 35

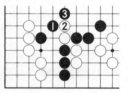

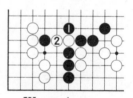

Correct Answer

After Black 1, the four white stones in the center cannot escape.

Wrong Answer

Attacking directly with 1 and 3 fails because the ladder doesn't work.

PROBLEM 36

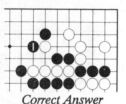

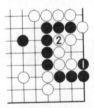

Correct Answer

Jumping ahead of the white stone with Black 1 leads to its capture.

Wrong Answer

Black 1 is a crude move that has no follow-up.

PROBLEM 37

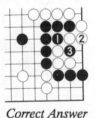

Correct Answer

Black 1, followed by 3, creates a shortage of liberties, preventing White from rescuing his three stones.

Wrong Answer

If Black plays 1, White connects with 2, and there is no way that Black can capture White's stones.

— 90 —

PROBLEM 38

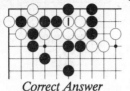

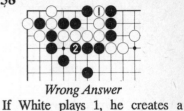

Correct Answer
White 1 is the vital point. The two black stones here can no longer avoid capture.

Wrong Answer
If White plays 1, he creates a shortage of liberties for his stones, so Black will capture them.

PROBLEM 39

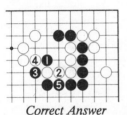

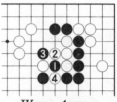

Correct Answer
Attaching with 1 is the vital point. Resistance by White with 2 and 4 is futile.

Wrong Answer
Black 1 and 3 lead nowhere. When White captures with 4, Black's attack has petered out.

PROBLEM 40

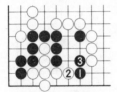

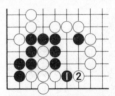

Correct Answer
Black 1 seals the fate of the six white stones. Resistance with 2 is futile.

Wrong Answer
If Black 1, White 2; Black can't keep the white stones on the left separated from the ones on the right.

PROBLEM 41

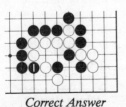

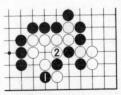

Correct Answer
If Black simply plays 1, White can't rescue his six stones.

Wrong Answer
After White plays 2, it is obvious that Black 1 has failed.

PROBLEM 42

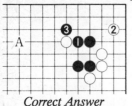

Correct Answer

Black should make a 'bamboo joint' with 1. White plays 2, and Black 3 or A is the joseki.

Wrong Answer

If Black plays 1, White will push through and cut with 2 and 4, leaving Black with an unsatisfactory position.

PROBLEM 43

Correct Answer

In this case, it is joseki to block at Black 1. If White now pushes through at A, Black responds with B.

Wrong Answer

In this position, 1 is a passive move which leaves Black at a disadvantage.

PROBLEM 44

Correct Answer

Blocking at 1 is the joseki. If White plays A, Black can block at B.

Wrong Answer

Black 1 lets White take the corner and Black gets no compensation.

PROBLEM 45

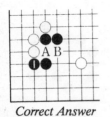

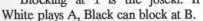

Correct Answer

Blocking at 1 is again correct. If White A, Black blocks at B.

Wrong Answer

Making a bamboo joint with 1 again leaves Black at a disadvantage.

PROBLEM 46

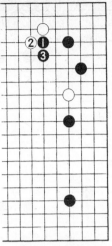

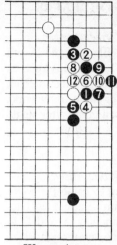

Correct Answer

Black should first attach and extend with 1 and 3. After making a wall at the top, he can attack the white stone on the right

Wrong Answer

If Black attaches underneath with 1, White plays the sequence to 12 and Black finds himself in an extremely unfavorable position.

PROBLEM 47

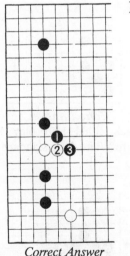

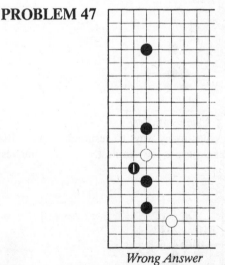

Correct Answer

Black should attack with 1 and 3. There are many possibilities after this, but none will be unfavorable for Black.

Wrong Answer

Moves such as Black 1, which is purely defensive, are inferior. In handicap games, it is important to think first and foremost of attacking White.

PROBLEM 48

Correct Answer

Both Black 1 and A are correct. In positions such as this, it is important to think of building large frameworks rather than going after single stones.

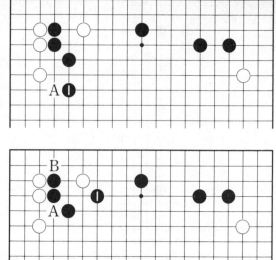

Wrong Answer

Trying to catch the white stone with Black 1 is bad. White can play A and B in sente and even though Black will capture the white stone, his result is unfavorable.

PROBLEM 49

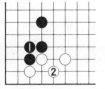

Correct Answer 1

Black has many ways to respond, but Black 1 here is the simplest.

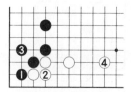

Correct Answer 2

Black could also play 1. The moves to White 4 are standard.

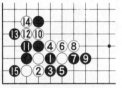

Correct Answer 3

There is also the sequence to 14, where Black takes the corner and gives White the outside.

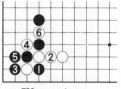

Wrong Answer

The sequence in this diagram would be bad for Black in almost every case.

PROBLEM 50

Correct Answer

White 1 is the best choice because this move establishes a base for White on the right.

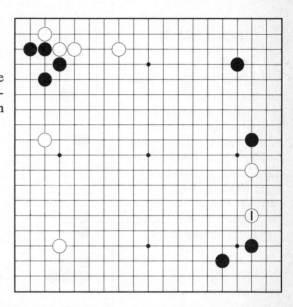

Wrong Answer

White 1 is bad. If White were going to play in this area, a move at 'a' would be standard. White 1 makes White overconcentrated: it strengthens an already secure position. White B is also bad. If White were going to play on the left side, 'b' would be the standard move.

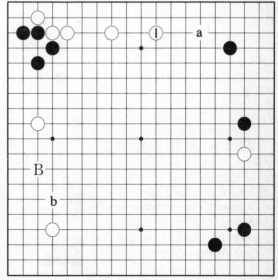

PROBLEM 51

Correct Answer

Black 1 is a good move because it is both an extension and an approach move. This move also establishes a secure base at the bottom for the three black stones there. This is important because White's stones on the left are strong, so Black's two stones at the bottom could come under attack.

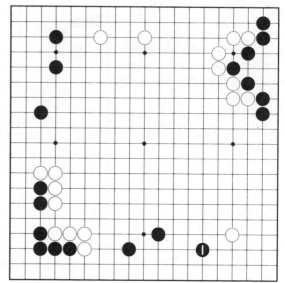

Wrong Answer

White would be grateful if Black were to play 1. He could then respond by playing a good attacking move at 'a'. Black C is certainly a good point, but it lacks the urgency of Black 1 in the Correct Answer diagram.

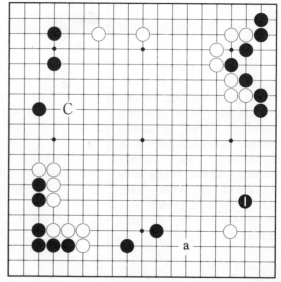

PROBLEM 52

Correct Answer

White 1 is a good move because it traps the lone black stone on the right side. If White were to play any other move, Black would play 'a' and what was previously a weak stone would now become a strong one.

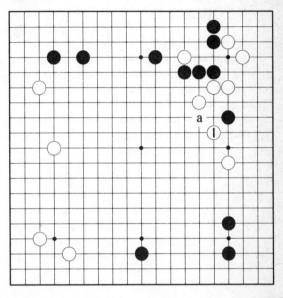

Wrong Answer

This is not the time for White to invade at 1. Nor should White play C, although locally, it is an excellent point. Were White to play either of these moves, Black would move out into the center with his stone on the upper right.

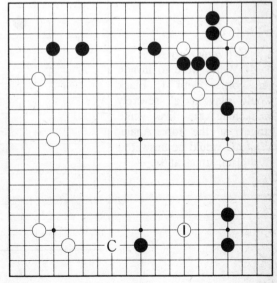

PROBLEM 53

Correct Answer
Jumping out into the center with 1 prevents an attack on White's stones at the top. There are many good moves on the left side and bottom that White could play, but they would let Black attack White by playing at 1.

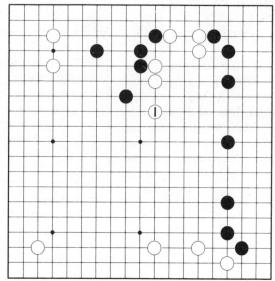

Wrong Answer
If White were to invade the corner with 1, Black would play at 'a', severely weakening the five white stones at the top. Again, White C would be answered by a black attack at 'b'.

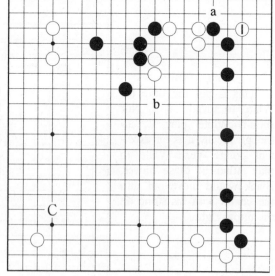

PROBLEM 54

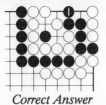

Correct Answer

When Black plays 1, the white stones are dead as they stand. If White were to struggle on —

Continuation 1

Black would answer White 2 by taking three stones with 3, winning the capturing race by one move.

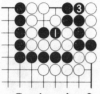

Continuation 2

If Black were called upon to prove that White's stones were dead, he could play 1 and 3, and again he wins the capturing race by one move.

Wrong Answer

Black 1, as the first move, enables White to take the vital point with 2. Now White can capture the black stones on the left on by winning a ko.

PROBLEM 55

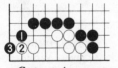

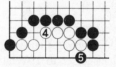

Correct Answer

After Black 1 and 3, White can't live.

Continuation

If White plays 4, Black plays 5 and it is clear that White is dead.

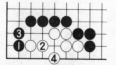

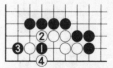

Wrong Answer 1

If Black attaches at 1, White lives with 2 and 4. Black 1 looks like a severe move, but it fails.

Wrong Answer 2

Black 1 also fails when White makes the obvious responses of 2 and 4.

PROBLEM 56

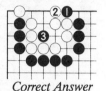

Correct Answer

Black kills White by attacking at 1. If White replies with 2, Black plays 3 and White is dead.

Wrong Answer

Black 1 is not the vital point. White can now turn the situation into a seki by playing the sequence to 6.

PROBLEM 57

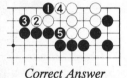

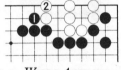

Correct Answer

If White tries to get a second eye with 2 and 4, Black kills him with 5.

Wrong Answer

Black 1 lets White easily make his second eye with 2.

PROBLEM 58

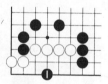

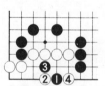

Correct Answer

If Black slides to 1, White is able to make only one eye, so he is dead.

Wrong Answer

Black 1 gives White too much space, so he can live with 2 and 4.

PROBLEM 59

Correct Answer

Attacking with Black 1 and 3 kills the white stones.

Wrong Answer

If Black ataris with 1, White will play 2 and live with ko.

PROBLEM 60

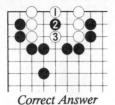

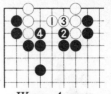

Correct Answer

If White plays on the central point with 1, he can easily live.

Wrong Answer

White 1 is on a central point, but the wrong one. 2 and 4 kill White.

PROBLEM 61

Correct Answer

White plays on the 2–1 point — the vital point of the corner. If Black defends his two stones with 2, White makes two eyes in the corner with 3.

Wrong Answer

White captures two stones, but he can't get a second eye after Black 2. If White instead plays at A, Black plays at 1 and White is dead.

PROBLEM 62

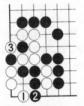

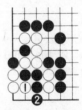

Correct Answer

White gets his eye in the corner when he plays 1. After 2, White gets his second eye by capturing with 3.

Wrong Answer

If White ataris with 1, he fails because after Black 2, he can't get his second eye in the corner.

PROBLEM 63

Correct Answer

By taking the 2–1 point with 1, White is able to make two eyes.

Wrong Answer

If White 1, Black will take the vital point with 2, killing White.

PROBLEM 64

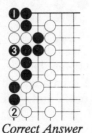

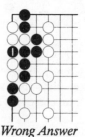

Correct Answer

If Black 1, White can't connect (it is illegal). He can then capture both groups of stones with one move.

Wrong Answer

If Black captures two stones with 1, White throws in a stone with 2, so Black is dead.

PROBLEM 65

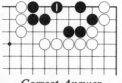

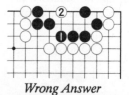

Correct Answer

Black 1 is the vital point for making two eyes.

Wrong Answer

If Black 1, White plays 2, and Black is dead.

PROBLEM 66

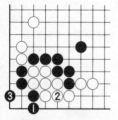

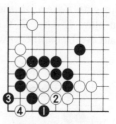

Correct Answer

Playing 1 gives Black two options for getting two eyes: 2 or 3. If White takes one, Black takes the other.

Wrong Answer

Playing atari with 1, followed by 3, fails. White plays 4 and Black is dead.

PROBLEM 67

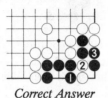

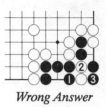

Correct Answer

Black lives with 1 and 3. If White captures the four stones on the right, Black ataris White's stones by playing on the point just above 2, getting his second eye when he captures them.

Wrong Answer
4: at 2

If Black immediately captures two stones with 3, White throws in with 4 and destroys Black's second eye.

PROBLEM 68

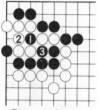

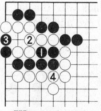

Correct Answer

Sacrificing a stone with 1 and giving atari with 3 kills the white stones.

Wrong Answer

The atari of Black 1 is too slow. Black loses the capturing race when White plays 4.

PROBLEM 69

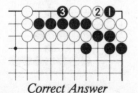

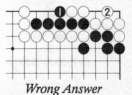

Correct Answer

Black 1 is the vital point. If White 2, White is dead after Black 3.

Wrong Answer

If Black lets White play 2, the position turns into a ko.

PROBLEM 70

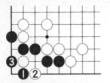

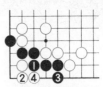

Correct Answer

Clamping with Black 1 is the vital point for creating a ko in the corner.

Wrong Answer

If Black plays 1, all his stones are dead as they stand after White 4.

PROBLEM 71

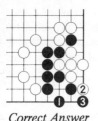

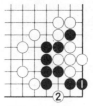

Correct Answer

Black 1 and 3 turn the corner into a ko. If Black wins this ko, he can get his second eye and live.

Wrong Answer

If Black plays 1, White strikes at the vital point with 2 and Black is dead.

PROBLEM 72

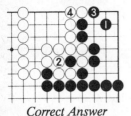

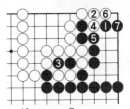

Correct Answer

Jumping to Black 1 is the correct answer. After this the sequence to White 4 follows.

Alternate Sequence

White could also play 2. Black would then capture with 3. The result is the same as in the correct answer.

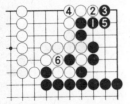

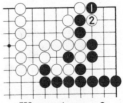

Wrong Answer 1

This result is two points worse for Black than the correct answer.

Wrong Answer 2

Blocking at 1 would result in a huge loss for Black.

PROBLEM 73

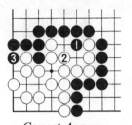

Correct Answer

Black 1 is correct. The points 2 and 3 have the same value: it doesn't matter which side takes them. White has nine points of territory.

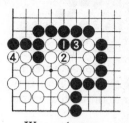

Wrong Answer

Black 1 is a mistake. After 4, White has ten points of territory.

PROBLEM 74

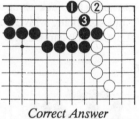

Correct Answer

Black can halt White's intrusion by playing 1 and 3.

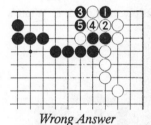

Wrong Answer

If Black 1 and 3, this result is four points worse than the correct answer.

PROBLEM 75

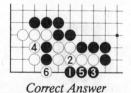

Correct Answer

Black 1 forces White to capture the two stones in the corner in the sequence to 6.

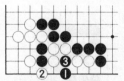

Reference Diagram

If White responds to 1 with 2, Black catches two white stones when he cuts with 3.

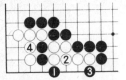

Wrong Answer 1

The sequence here is two points inferior to the correct answer.

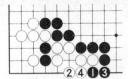

Wrong Answer 2

The sequence here is four points inferior to the correct answer.

PROBLEM 76

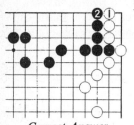

Correct Answer

Simply playing 1 is White's best move.

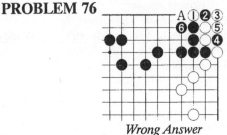

Wrong Answer

White expects Black to answer 1 with A, but sacrificing with 2 and 4 is better. Later Black can play A.

PROBLEM 77

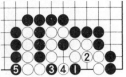

Correct Answer

Black 1 takes advantage of White's shortage of liberties. After Black 5, White can't connect at 3.

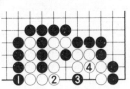

Wrong Answer

Black 1 and 3 fail. After 4, White's group has two eyes.

PROBLEM 78

Correct Answer

Black 1 is the most profitable move.

Wrong Answer

If Black 1, White 2. This result is three points worse for Black.

PROBLEM 79

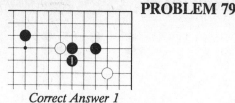

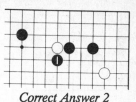

Correct Answer 1

Black 1 is the standard response. Black plans to fight on a grand scale.

Correct Answer 2

Black 1 here is the severest move, but the aptness of this move depends on the surrounding position.

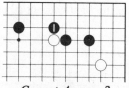

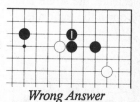

Correct Answer 3

Black 1 is the safest response. Here Black is playing for territory.

Wrong Answer

Black 1 is too tight and submissive. In almost all cases, it is inferior.

PROBLEM 80

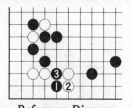

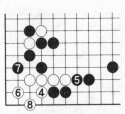

Correct Answer

Black 1 is severe. It is the standard follow-up to the joseki position in the problem diagram.

Continuation

White can live with the moves to 8, but Black has made a big gain.

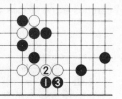

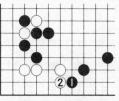

Reference Diagram

White can't resist with 2, since he will be split into two groups when Black plays 3.

Wrong Answer

An endgame move like Black 1 enables White to settle his stones without any problems.

PROBLEM 81

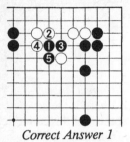

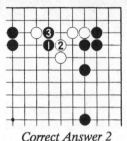

Correct Answer 1

Striking at 1 is severe. Up to 5, Black catches the stone and gets influence down the right side.

Correct Answer 2

If White 2, Black plays 3, catching a stone and leaving the four white stones on the right without a base.

PROBLEM 82

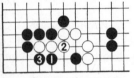

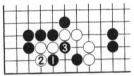

Correct Answer

Black 1 is a brilliant tesuji. Black not only takes profit but also launches a severe attack on White.

Reference Diagram

If White resists with 2, Black cuts off and catches three stones with 3.

PROBLEM 83

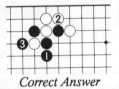

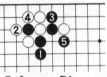

Correct Answer

Black 1 is a tesuji. If White 2, Black catches a stone in a ladder with 3 .

Reference Diagram

If White replies with 2, Black builds a position on the right up to 5.

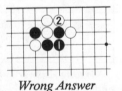

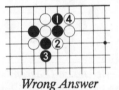

Wrong Answer

If Black connects at 1, he has no effective follow-up after White 2.

Wrong Answer

If 1, White captures two stones with 2 and 4. This is bad for Black.

PROBLEM 84

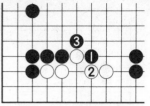

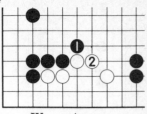

Correct Answer
The clamp of 1 enables Black to keep White confined to the bottom.

Wrong Answer
Black 1 allows White to move out into the center with 2.

PROBLEM 85

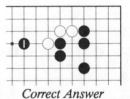

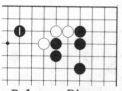

Correct Answer
Black 1 is the standard attack on White's three stones.

Reference Diagram
Black's position is strong, so Black 1 here is also a good move.

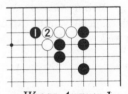

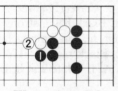

Wrong Answer 1
Black 1 helps White to defend his cutting point with 2.

Wrong Answer 2
Black 1 is also bad. It helps White to strengthen his position.

PROBLEM 86

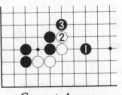

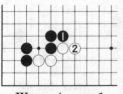

Correct Answer
Just like in the preceding problem Black 1 is correct. If White 2, Black applies pressure with 3.

Wrong Answer 1
As before, Black 1 is a bad move. *(The answer to this problem is continued on the next page.)*

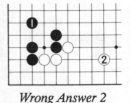

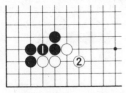

Wrong Answer 2

Black 1 is too passive. Black can now take the opportunity to stabilize his position at the bottom with 2.

Wrong Answer 3

Black 1 is almost meaningless. White stabilizes his position by defending the cutting point with 2.

PROBLEM 87

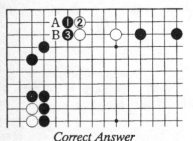

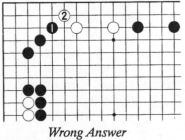

Correct Answer

Since Black has a strong position on the left, he can jump as far as 1. If White 2, Black plays 3. If White 2 at 3, Black A. If White 2 at B, Black 3.

Wrong Answer

Black 1 lets White expand his position to 2.

PROBLEM 88

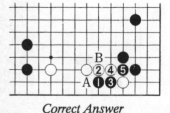

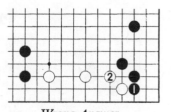

Correct Answer

Black can take profit by playing the moves to 5. In some cases, Black might play 3 at A. If White 2 at 4, Black 2, White B, Black A.

Wrong Answer

Black 1 lets White defend his weak point with 2.

PROBLEM 89

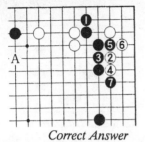

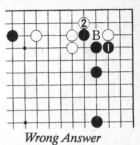

Correct Answer

Black 1 is correct. Even though White can live in the corner, he does so in gote and Black can then proceed to attack the three white stones at the top by jumping to A.

Wrong Answer

Black 1 is too passive. White can stabilize his stones at the top with 2. Black 1 at B is a special strategy, but it is inferior in most cases.

PROBLEM 90

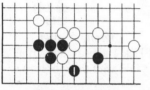

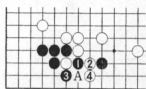

Correct Answer

Black 1 is the tesuji that ensures all black stones will be connected.

Wrong Answer

The atari of Black 1 lets White isolate the black stone on the right with 2 and 4. However, Black 1 at 3 results in a ko when White plays A, Black 1, White 2.

PROBLEM 91

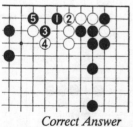

Correct Answer

Black strikes at the vital point with 1 and then robs White of his base with 3 and 5. If White plays 4 at 5, Black plays 5 at 4.

Wrong Answer

Black 1 is unsatisfactory since it lets White patch up his defect by playing at 2.

PROBLEM 92

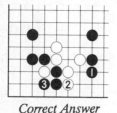

Correct Answer

If Black 1, the five white stones in the center become weak after the exchange of 2 for 3.

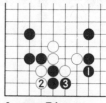

Reference Diagram

White 2 is unreasonable. Black plays 3 and the two white stones in the corner will be captured.

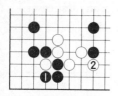

Wrong Answer 1

Black 1 enables White to make a strong position for his stones with 2.

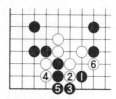

Wrong Answer 2

Black 1 aims to link up all stones, but it fails with the moves to 6.

PROBLEM 93

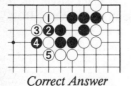

Correct Answer

White 1 is the vital point. After the moves to White 5 —

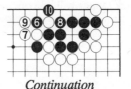

Continuation

White plays 7 and 9, confining Black to the top and ending in sente.

Wrong Answer 1

If White plays the moves to 7, he still confines Black but ends in gote.

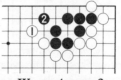

Wrong Answer 2

White gets sente with 1, but after 2, he has failed to confine Black.

PROBLEM 94

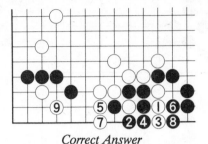

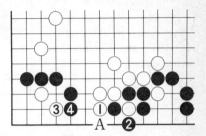

Correct Answer

White must first play 1 and 3, then force Black to capture these stones with 5 and 7. This being done, White can link up with his stone in the corner by playing 9.

Wrong Answer

Simply playing 1 and 3 is not good enough. Black plays 4, and White A is not a threat to the black stones on the right. The two white stones in the corner now die.

PROBLEM 95

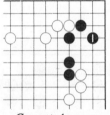

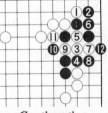

Correct Answer

Black 1 is the move that enables Black to live in the most profitable way.

Continuation

White attacks with 1 and 3, but Black counterattacks with the moves to 12. All his stones are connected and he can easily get two eyes.

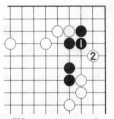

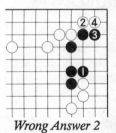

Wrong Answer 1

Connecting at 1 invites White to slide to 2. Black must still struggle to make two eyes.

Wrong Answer 2

If Black plays 1, then after White 2 and 4 he still doesn't have two eyes.

PROBLEM 96

Correct Answer
Because of Black's extremely thick position on the left, White should extend no farther than 1.

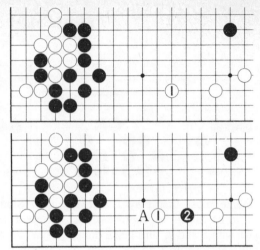

Wrong Answer
Extending as far as 1 (or A) invites a black invasion at 2. White will be at a disadvantage because of Black's thick position.

PROBLEM 97

Correct Answer
Black 1 aims at two cutting points, 2 and 3. If White 2 at 3, Black cuts at 2 and capture four white stones.

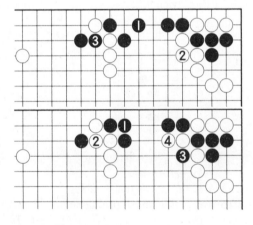

Wrong Answer
If Black plays 1, White can connect at 2. Black 3 now fails to capture any white stones.

PROBLEM 98

Correct Answer
Black can defend his stones at the bottom in sente by peeping with 1.

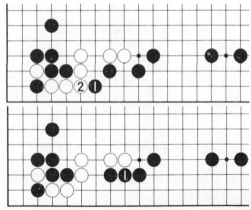

Wrong Answer
Black 1 is a strong connection, but Black ends in gote.

PROBLEM 99

Correct Answer
White 1 creates a double threat. If Black 2 at 3, White plays 3 at 2 and captures the two black stones.

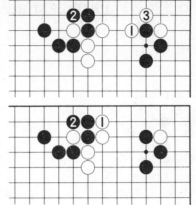

Wrong Answer
White 1 makes no threat against the corner. After Black 2, White has no follow-up moves.

PROBLEM 100

Correct Answer
White first plays 1 and then cuts with 3. His strategy is to sacrifice two stones to build up thickness and make good shape.

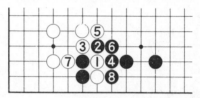

Wrong Answer
White should be careful not to play 3. This will result in a slightly inferior position for White.

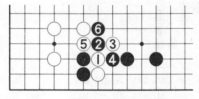

PROBLEM 101

Correct Answer
Black 1 ensures the capture of White's stones on the right. If White 2, Black captures five stones after 5. If White 2 at 3, Black plays 3 one line below 2.

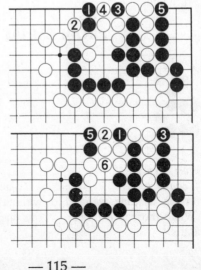

Wrong Answer
The order of moves is important. If Black plays 1 first, White saves all his stones when he plays 6.

PROBLEM 102

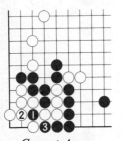

Correct Answer

Black throws in a stone with 1 and ataris with 3.

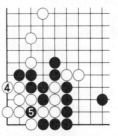

Continuation

White must make his second eye with 4, letting Black to capture four white stones.

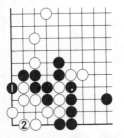

Wrong Answer 1

If Black 1, White can easily live with 2. The black stones above are now in for a severe fight.

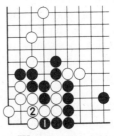

Wrong Answer 2

Black 1 is too crude. White gets eye shape by simply defending with 2.

PROBLEM 103

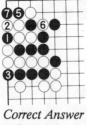

Correct Answer
4: connects

Black throws in a stone with 1 and captures White through a series of successive ataris.

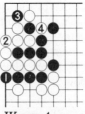

Wrong Answer

Black cannot capture White without first sacrificing a stone, as this diagram shows.

PROBLEM 104

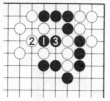

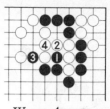

Correct Answer

Black wedges in with 1. After 3, the three white stones can't escape.

Wrong Answer

Black 1 and 3 are artless. White connects to the outside with 2 and 4.

PROBLEM 105

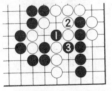

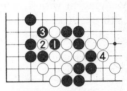

Correct Answer

Black 1 is the only way to capture White's stones.

Wrong Answer

Sacrificing with 1 may seem like a tesuji, but the position is now a ko.

PROBLEM 106

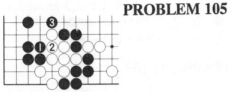

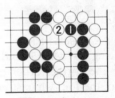

Correct Answer

Black 1 is the vital point for separating the three stones at the bottom from the ones above.

Wrong Answer

Black 1 is too slow. After White 2, Black can no longer rescue his stones to the right.

PROBLEM 107

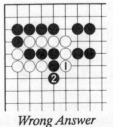

Correct Answer

White captures Black by jumping ahead with 1. Up to 9, Black escapes.

Wrong Answer

White 1 is an artless move. White's position is now hopeless.

PROBLEM 108

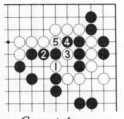

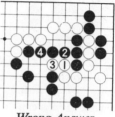

Correct Answer

By wedging in with 1, White can capture three stones. If Black 2, White 3 and 5 block Black's escape.

Wrong Answer

Black 1 and 3 are artless moves. White can connect to his outside stones with 2 and 4.

PROBLEM 109

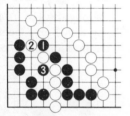

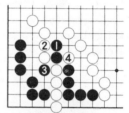

Correct Answer

Wedging in with 1 and cutting with 3 is the correct order of moves to capture the four white stones.

Wrong Answer

If Black plays 1 and 3, White will win the capturing race by one move after he plays 4.

PROBLEM 110

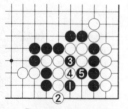

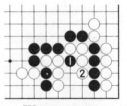

Correct Answer

Attaching with 1 is the key move. The three white stones will be captured after Black 3 and 5.

Wrong Answer

Sacrificing with 1 is premature. All of White's stones now live, so seven black stones will be captured.

PROBLEM 111

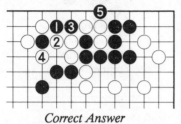

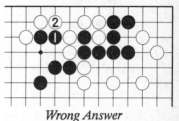

Correct Answer

Black can capture White with the moves to 5. Black's eight stones in the corner are now alive. If White 2 at 3, Black catches White with 2.

Wrong Answer

If Black plays 1, he has no follow-up after White 2.

PROBLEM 112

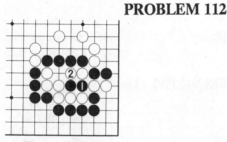

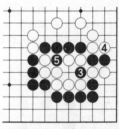

Correct Answer

Sacrificing two stones with 1 is a brilliant move. When White captures with 2 —

Continuation

Black plays 3 and 5 and captures six white stones.

PROBLEM 113

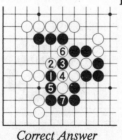

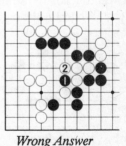

Correct Answer

The attachment at 1 is the vital point. If White resists, his stones are captured with the moves to 7.

Wrong Answer

White can easily escape to the outside if Black plays 1.

PROBLEM 114

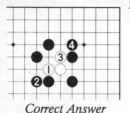

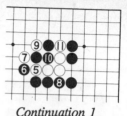

Correct Answer
Playing 1 and 3 in either order is correct.

Continuation 1
White escapes with the sequence to 11.

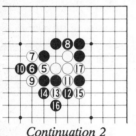

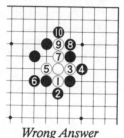

Continuation 2
In answer to 7, Black might play 8, but White escapes up to 17.

Wrong Answer
White fails to escape with 1 and 3 here, as the continuation here shows.

PROBLEM 115

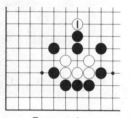

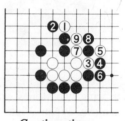

Correct Answer
"In a symmetrical position, play on the central point!" Strange as it may seem, White 1 is the only move.

Continuation
With the moves to 9, White has broken out of Black's enclosure.

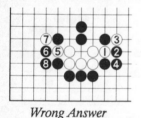

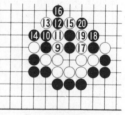

Wrong Answer
Direct moves, such as the ones shown here, fail.

Continuation
The moves to Black 20 show why. These last two problems come from a classical Chinese problem book.

PROBLEM 116

Correct Answer

Black expands his right-side territory with 1 and 3 while attacking White's base. This position is reached in the famous Chinese Opening.

Wrong Answer

Black 1 enables White to expand his base with 2 while encroaching on Black's territory on the upper right side.

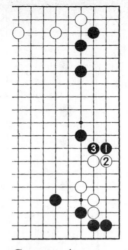
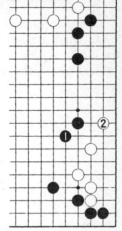

Correct Answer   *Wrong Answer*

PROBLEM 117

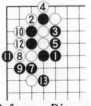

Correct Answer 1

Black can sacrifice a stone with 1, force once with 3 and then play 5. This result is advantageous for Black.

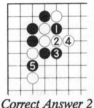

Correct Answer 2

If Black wants to develop a position at the top, he can start with 1 and play the moves to 7.

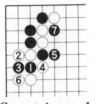

Reference Diagram

Depending on the situation, it may not necessarily be bad for Black to play 1. White would get the corner and Black outside influence.

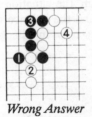

Wrong Answer

Black lives in the corner with 1 and 3, but White's outside influence leaves Black with an inferior position.

PROBLEM 118

Correct Answer

White must defend his corner territory with 1. To see why, look at the next Diagram.

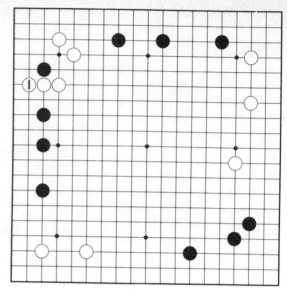

Wrong Answer

If White extends to 1, Black can live in the corner with the moves to 10. White 1 in the correct answer results in more than 15 points of white territory. In this diagram, the situation is reversed, and the balance of territory is now in Black's favor.

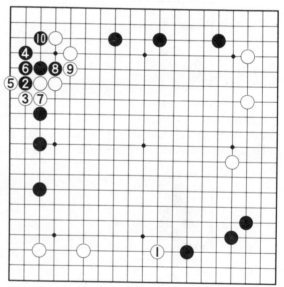

PROBLEM 119

Correct Answer

In the opening, there are certain points that have to be played before taking the big points on the side. Black 1 (as well as 3) is a typical example. These two moves give Black a huge territorial framework throughout the center of the board.

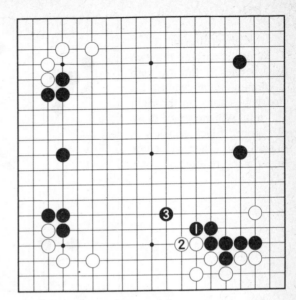

Wrong Answer

If Black takes the big point at the top with 1, White 2 flattens out Black's territorial framework. This move also expands White's territory at the bottom. It should be obvious now that this is the key point of the whole position.

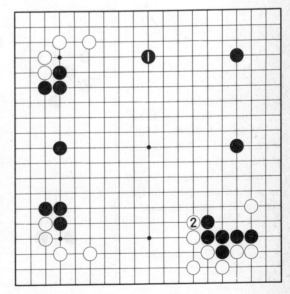

PROBLEM 120

Correct Answer

White separates the two black stones at the top with 1, pinning them against his strong positions on the right and left. Whichever of these two stones Black chooses to defend, the other will come under a severe attack.

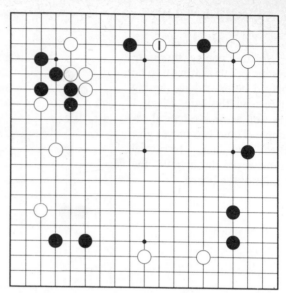

Wrong Answer

White 1 provokes Black to play a move which strengthens his thin position at the top with 2.

Locally, White A would be a good move, but in this position it misses the point.

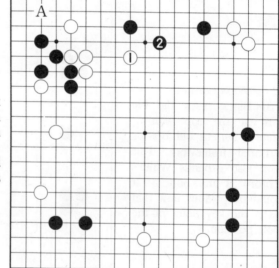

PROBLEM 121

Correct Answer
Black 1 is a strong move because it attacks the two white stones on the left, while defending Black's position at the bottom.

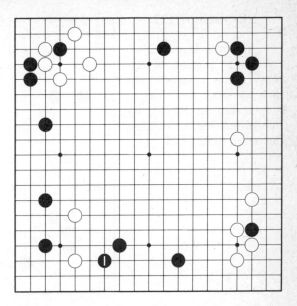

Wrong Answer
In some cases, Black 1 would be a good way to attack the two white stones. Here, however, White can invade with 2, severely attacking Black's two stones at the bottom. Therefore, Black 1 is in the wrong direction.

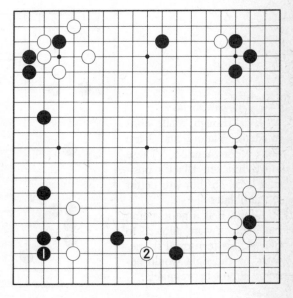

PROBLEM 122

Correct Answer

This is a game of territory versus influence. The time has come for White to put a stop to Black's influence-building, so he plays the moves from 1 to 5.

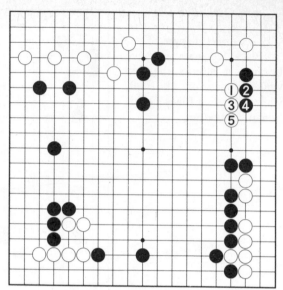

Wrong Answer

Even though White ends in sente, White 1 and 3 are not recommended. These moves thicken Black's position here, so they are better left until later.

White B is a good point, but if Black were allowed to play A, his territorial framework on the right would become almost impregnable.

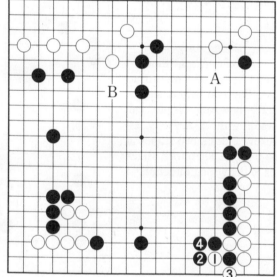

PROBLEM 123

Correct Answer

White should build a framework on the right by playing at 1. To see why this move is important, look at the next diagram.

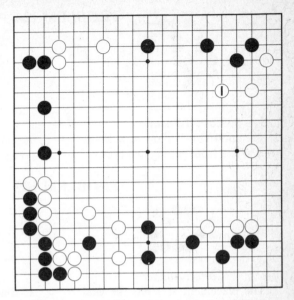

Wrong Answer

If White slides to 1, Black's strong position at the top makes 2 a good invasion. The key to victory or defeat lies in White's building up his right side with 1 in the Correct Answer Diagram.

Until White has reinforced his right side, an invasion at B is unreasonable.

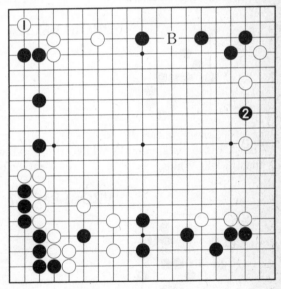

PROBLEM 124

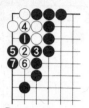

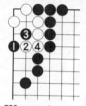

Correct Answer
The moves to 7 show how Black stops White from getting two eyes.

Wrong Answer
Against 1, White 2 is an effective response. After 4, White is alive.

PROBLEM 125

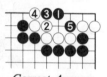

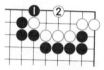

Correct Answer
The placement at 1 hits the vital point. After 5, White is helpless because of a shortage of liberties.

Wrong Answer
If Black 1, White takes the vital point himself with 2. It is now impossible for Black to kill White.

PROBLEM 126

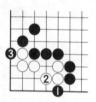

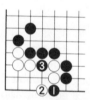

Correct Answer 1
Black 1 is the vital point. If White 2, Black 3 kills White.

Correct Answer 2
Answering 1 with 2, makes it even easier for Black to kill White with 3.

PROBLEM 127

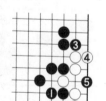

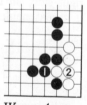

Correct Answer
Black must quietly pull back with 1. After 2, Black 3 and 5 kill White.

Wrong Answer
The atari of Black 1 makes it easy for White.

PROBLEM 128

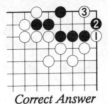

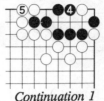

Correct Answer

The hane of 1, followed by the placement of 3, kills Black's stones.

Continuation 1

If Black continues with 4, White 5 seals the fate of Black's stones.

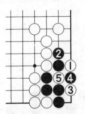

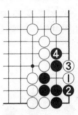

Continuation 2

White could reverse the order of 1 and 3. Again White 5 kills Black.

Wrong Answer

If White 1, Black easily lives by playing 2.

PROBLEM 129

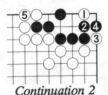

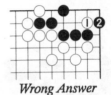

Correct Answer

After White 1 and 3, Black 4 turns this position into a ko.

Wrong Answer

White 1 fails. Black unconditionally has two eyes after he plays 4.

PROBLEM 130

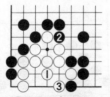

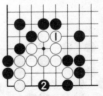

Correct Answer

White 1 is the key move. Black destroys White's eye above, but the situation becomes a ko with White 3.

Wrong Answer

If White makes an eye with 1, Black 2 kills any chance of White's making a second eye at the bottom.

PROBLEM 131

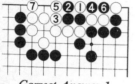

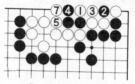

Correct Answer 1

If White 1, he can force Black to capture the stones in the corner with 3 and 5, then make his second eye with 7.

Correct Answer 2

6: captures four stones at 2

If Black answers with 2, White plays 3 to 7. Black must defend, so White can make his second eye.

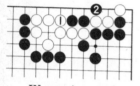

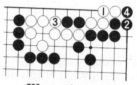

Wrong Answer 1

If White 1, Black ataris two white stones with 2. There is now no way for White to make his second eye.

Wrong Answer 2

If White 1, Black attacks from the other side with 2 and 4. Again White can't make his second eye.

PROBLEM 132

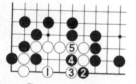

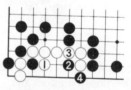

Correct Answer

White 1 enables White to live. He is alive after 5.

Wrong Answer 1

If White 1, Black attacks with 2 and 4.

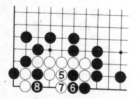

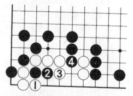

Continuation

If White resists with 5 and 7, Black 8 destroys White's eye shape.

Wrong Answer 2

White 1 here also fails, as the moves to Black 4 shows.

PROBLEM 133

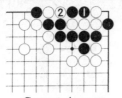

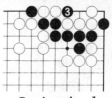

Correct Answer
Black sacrifices two stones with 1. After White captures with 2 —

Continuation 1
Black takes two stones with 3. Next —

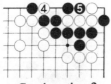

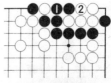

Continuation 2
White throws in at 4, returning to the original position. If both sides persist, the game ends in 'no result'.

Wrong Answer
If Black connects at 1, White 2 creates a 5-point nakade, so Black is dead.

Problem 134

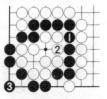

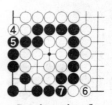

Correct Answer
Black must first play 1, linking up all his stones. After White 2, 3 gives Black eye shape.

Continuation 1
After all the liberties are filled, you can clearly see that Black really does have two eyes.

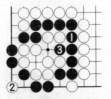

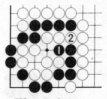

Continuation 2
If White tries to destroy the corner eyes with 2, Black ataris with 3, so White's stones will die.

Wrong Answer
If Black 1, White 2 kills all the black stones.

PROBLEM 135

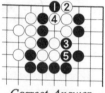

Correct Answer

After Black 5, White finds that he can't connect his three stones because he is short of liberties.

Wrong Answer

The order of moves is important, as this diagram shows. After White 4, it is Black that loses three stones.

PROBLEM 136

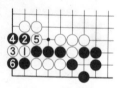

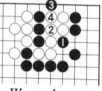

Correct Answer

Black 1 is a standard tesuji. After 5, Black captures three stones on his next move.

Wrong Answer

Again the order of moves is important, as you can see from this diagram.

PROBLEM 137

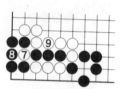

Correct Answer

White first sacrifices two stones with the moves to 5. After Black captures with 6 —

Continuation

White sacrifices another stone with 7. After White plays 9, it is clear that Black loses the capturing race.

PROBLEM 138

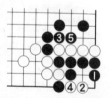

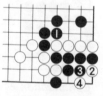

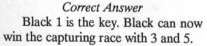

Correct Answer

Black 1 is the key. Black can now win the capturing race with 3 and 5.

Wrong Answer

If Black starts by filling an outside liberty with 1, a ko results after 4.

PROBLEM 139

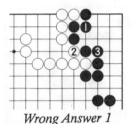

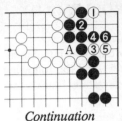

Correct Answer

Connecting at Black 1 is the correct answer. Next —

Continuation

These moves show that Black is secure. A is *not* sente for White.

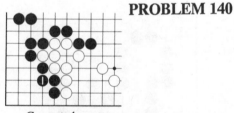

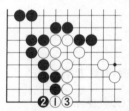

Wrong Answer 1

If Black 1, White 2 is now sente for White.

Wrong Answer 2

If Black 1, White 2 is sente. These two diagrams are two points worse than the correct answer.

PROBLEM 140

Correct Answer

Black 1 is the correct answer. The reason is shown in the next diagrams.

Reference Diagram 1

White 1 and 3 end in gote. But —

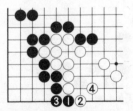

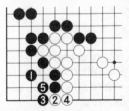

Reference Diagram 2

Black 1 and 3 are sente, so Black can play these moves before White.

Wrong Answer

If Black 1, White 2 and 4 are sente. This is a four-point loss for Black.

PROBLEM 141

Correct Answer
The diagonal attachment of White 1 and the following moves devastate Black's territory.

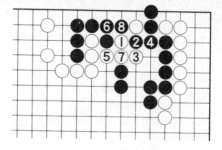

Wrong Answer
White 1 and 3 are answered by 2 and 4. White's incursion into Black's territory is minimal.

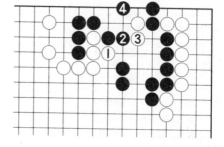

PROBLEM 142

Correct Answer
White 1 threatens to play both 3 and 'a'.

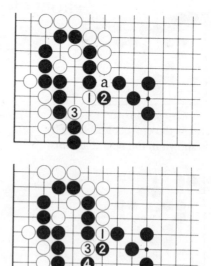

Wrong Answer
Playing White 1 first is artless. White now has no effective follow-up.

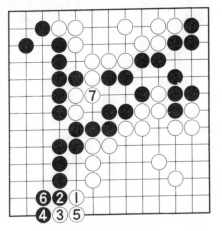

Correct Answer

White 1 is the biggest move, worth 6 points in double sente. After the sequence to 6, White connects at 7.

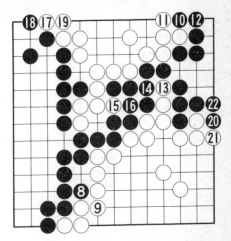

Continuation 1

The next biggest point is now 10. The game continues with the moves to 22. White has 45 points of territory, while Black has 42 points. White wins by 3 points.

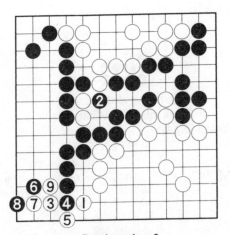

Continuation 2

Ignoring White 1 and cutting with 2 will not change the result in the preceding diagram, in spite of White's incursion in the lower left corner. Check this for yourself.

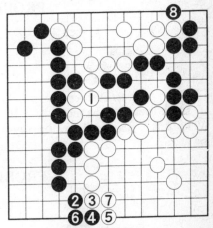

Wrong Answer

If White connects at 1, Black plays the sequence to 6 in sente, then takes the point 8. In this case, it is Black who wins by 3 points.

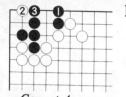 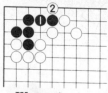

PROBLEM 144

Correct Answer
If Black plays 1, he will live no matter how White attacks.

Wrong Answer
If Black 1, White plays 2. There is now no way that Black can live.

PROBLEM 145

Correct Answer
Black 1 is the vital point. If White plays 2, Black 3. If White 2 at 3, Black 3 at 2. After this, no matter how White attacks, Black will live.

Wrong Answer
Black 1 here may seem equivalent to Black 1 in the correct answer. But there is a great difference. After White 2, Black is dead.

PROBLEM 146

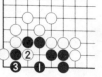 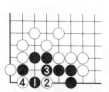

Correct Answer
Black lives with the moves to 3. If White 2 at 3, Black still lives by playing at 2.

Wrong Answer
If Black plays 1, White 2 and 4 result in a ko.

PROBLEM 147

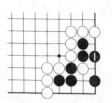 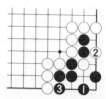

Correct Answer
Black 1 is the most profitable way for Black to make two eyes.

Reference Diagram
Black can also live with 1 and 3, but White catches two stones with 2.

PROBLEM 148

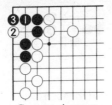

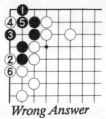

Correct Answer
Black can live by playing 1 and 3

Wrong Answer
Playing on the 1–2 point with Black 1 doesn't work. After White 6, Black's stones are dead.

PROBLEM 149

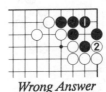

Correct Answer
Black can live by playing 1 and 3.

Wrong Answer
Black 1 results in a ko after White plays 2.

PROBLEM 150

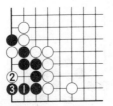

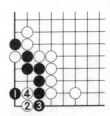

Correct Answer
Black can live by playing 1 and 3.

Wrong Answer
Black 1 is refuted by White 2 and 4. Note that if the white stone in atari were not present, Black could live.

PROBLEM 151

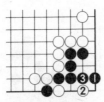

Correct Answer
Black lives by playing 1 and 3.

Wrong Answer
If Black 1, White can kill Black with 2 and 4. Compare this problem to the preceding one.

PROBLEM 152

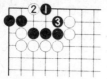

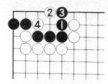

Correct Answer

Black lives by playing 1 and 3.

Wrong Answer

Black 1 fails. White 2 and 4 create a shortage of liberties for Black.

PROBLEM 153

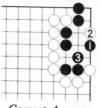

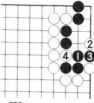

Correct Answer

Black 1 is the move that covers Black's shortage of liberties. If White 2, Black lives with 3.

Wrong Answer

If Black plays 1, his shortage of liberties suddenly becomes clear when White plays 2 and 4.

PROBLEM 154

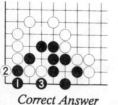

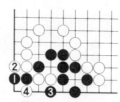

Correct Answer

Descending to 1 is the only way Black can live. If White 2, Black catches two stones with 3 and lives.

Wrong Answer

Black can't live if he plays 1. White will capture these two stones by playing 2 and 4.

PROBLEM 155

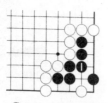

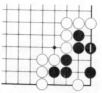

Correct Answer 1

Black 1 gives him two eyes and life.

Correct Answer 2

Black can also live with 1 here. These two moves are the only moves that give Black two eyes.

PROBLEM 156

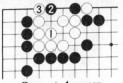

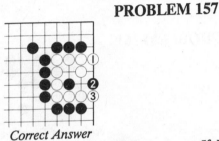

Correct Answer
White lives by playing 1 and 3.

Wrong Answer
If White plays 1, Black kills all the white stones by playing 2.

PROBLEM 157

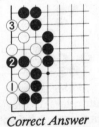

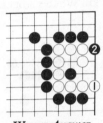

Correct Answer
White can live in seki by playing 1 and 3.

Wrong Answer
If White plays 1, his stones are dead after Black plays 2.

PROBLEM 158

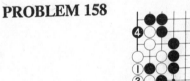

Correct Answer
Connecting at 1 enables White to live. If Black 2 at 3, White 3 at 2. Either way, White gets two eyes.

Wrong Answer
If White plays 1, Black can kill him by playing 2 and 4.

PROBLEM 159

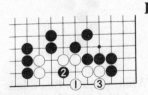

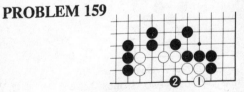

Correct Answer
White gets two eyes with 1 and 3. Black's stone at 2 cannot escape.

Wrong Answer
White 1 is refuted by Black 2. White is now dead.

PROBLEM 160

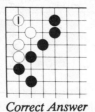

Correct Answer

White lives by playing at 1. No matter how he attacks, there is now no way to kill White's stones.

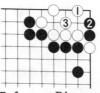

Wrong Answer

If White plays 1, Black kills him by playing 2.

PROBLEM 161

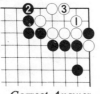

Correct Answer

One way for White to live is by playing 1 and 3.

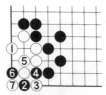

Reference Diagram

Two other ways for White to live is to play 1 and 3 in either order.

PROBLEM 162

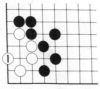

Correct Answer

Because White's two stones have two liberties on the outside, White can live with 1.

Wrong Answer

If White plays 1, Black can turn this position into a ko with the sequence to 7.

PROBLEM 163

Correct Answer

Since White's two stones have two liberties on the outside, White can get two eyes with 1. If Black 2, White easily lives with 3.

Wrong Answer

If White plays 1, Black kills him with 2 and 4.

PROBLEM 164

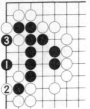

Correct Answer
Black first plays 1 and then 3. White can't capture 3 without losing two of his own stones. If Black 2 at 3, White plays 2.

Wrong Answer
There is no follow-up to Black 1. Now all of Black's stones die.

PROBLEM 165

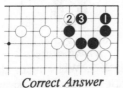

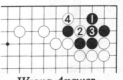

Correct Answer
The only way Black can live is by playing 1. If White 2, Black 3.

Wrong Answer
Black 1 looks like good shape, but White kills Black with 2 and 4.

PROBLEM 166

Correct Answer
Black can unconditionally live by playing at 1.

Wrong Answer
If Black 1, the position turns into a ko when White plays 2 and 4.

PROBLEM 167

Correct Answer
Black plays the vital point of 1 and then makes two eyes with 3.

Wrong Answer
If Black ataris a stone with 1, White takes the vital point with 2 and Black is dead. If Black 1 at A, White 2 at 1 and Black is dead.

PROBLEM 168

Correct Answer

If Black plays 1, followed by 3, White will have to give up three stones after Black plays 5.

Wrong Answer

Black cannot capture any stones by playing 1 first. White will connect with 2; Black 3 will be captured.

PROBLEM 169

Correct Answer

Black 1 is the vital point. When White ataris with 7, White cannot rescue his three stones.

Wrong Answer

If Black 1, White takes the vital point with 2. The black stones are now dead.

PROBLEM 170

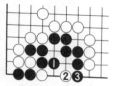

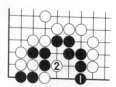

Correct Answer

Black can live with 1 and 3.

Wrong Answer

If Black 1, White kills Black with 2. If Black takes a white stone with 1, White kills Black by playing at 1.

PROBLEM 171

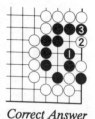

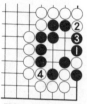

Correct Answer

Black can live with 1. This is exactly the same kind of move as in the preceding problem.

Wrong Answer

Black dies if he captures a stone with 1, as the moves to White 4 show.

PROBLEM 172

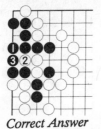

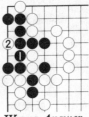

Correct Answer

Black 1 is the vital point. If White 2, Black ataris the three white stones and gets his second eye.

Wrong Answer

If Black plays 1, White destroys Black's eye shape by playing at 2.

PROBLEM 173

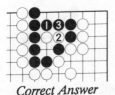

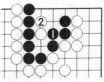

Correct Answer

Black gets two eyes with 1 and 3. Note that White can't capture the stone in atari because of a snapback.

Wrong Answer

If Black connects at 1, White plays 2 and Black dies because he has a 3-point nakade.

PROBLEM 174

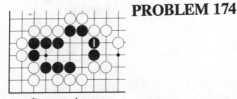

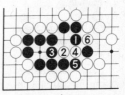

Correct Answer

Black 1 is the vital point. No matter how White attacks, he can't kill Black.

Wrong Answer

Black 1 is not only small in scale, it also results in the death of Black's stones after White plays 6.

PROBLEM 175

Correct Answer

Black lives by playing on the 1–2 point, the vital point.

Wrong Answer

Black 1 looks big, but 2 turns Black's shape into a 5-point nakade.

PROBLEM 176

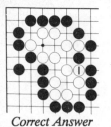

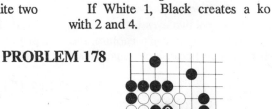

Correct Answer

White secures his two eyes, one at the the top and the other at the bottom, by playing at 1.

Wrong Answer

If Black is allowed to play 2, White can no longer make an eye at the top.

PROBLEM 177

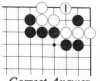

Correct Answer

Simply playing 1 gives White two eyes.

Wrong Answer

If White 1, Black creates a ko with 2 and 4.

PROBLEM 178

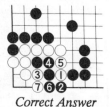

Correct Answer

Wedging in with 1 is the tesuji for getting two eyes. The moves to White 7 show how White does this.

Wrong Answer

The order of moves is important, as this diagram illustrates.

PROBLEM 179

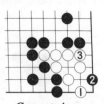

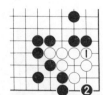

Correct Answer

Black 1 is the tesuji. If Black 2, White gets two eyes with 3. If Black 2 at 3, White 3 at 2.

Wrong Answer

The order of moves is important. If White plays 1 first, Black 2 kills the white stones.

PROBLEM 180

Correct Answer
Black 1 is the vital point for getting two eyes.

Wrong Answer
If Black 1, White can turn the corner into a ko with the moves to 6.

PROBLEM 181

Correct Answer
Black lives by playing 1 and 3. If White 2 at 3, Black gets his second eye by playing 3 at 2.

Wrong Answer
Black 1 fails, as the moves to White 8 demonstrate.

PROBLEM 182

Correct Answer
Black 1 renders the white stone harmless and ensures two eyes for Black's group.

Wrong Answer
However, if Black plays 1, White 2 and 4 turn the corner into a ko.

PROBLEM 183

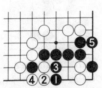

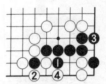

Correct Answer
Black get two eyes for his group with the moves to 5. If White 2 at 5, Black 3 at 4.

Wrong Answer
If Black plays 1, White 2 and 4 link up with the two white stones in the corner, so Black's stones die.

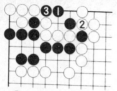

PROBLEM 184

Correct Answer 1

Black 1 and 3 will capture the four white stones in the corner, so all of Black's stones live.

Correct Answer 2

If White plays 2 in answer to 1, Black 3 will also capture the four white corner stones.

PROBLEM 185

Correct Answer

Black 1, aiming for eye shape, is the vital point. If White captures with 2, Black 3 makes the second eye.

Wrong Answer

If Black defends the stone in atari, White strikes at the vital point and Black is dead.

PROBLEM 186

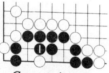

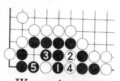

Correct Answer

Black 1 ensures life for all of the black stones.

Wrong Answer

Black can also live with 1, but in the process he loses his three stones on the right.

PROBLEM 187

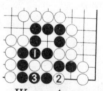

Correct Answer
5: played above 1

Black 1 is the vital point. White can capture four stones with 4, but Black comes back with 5 and captures three of White's.

Wrong Answer
4: throws in between 1 and 2

If Black captures two stones with 1 and 3, White creates a false eye with 2 and 4.

— 146 —

PROBLEM 188

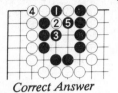

Correct Answer

Sacrificing a stone with 1 and then playing 3 and 5 enable Black to get two eyes.

Wrong Answer

Black 1 is a move without any follow-up.

PROBLEM 189

Correct Answer

Black sacrifices a stone and then makes two eyes with 3 and 5.

Wrong Answer

Black 1 and 3 are artless moves. When White plays 4, Black is dead.

PROBLEM 190

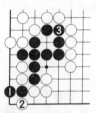

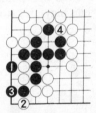

Correct Answer

When Black plays 1, the two white stones are as good as captured. If White 2 at 3, Black 3 at 2. Either way, Black gets two eyes.

Wrong Answer

Black 1 is too slow. This gives White time to play both 2 and 4, leaving Black with only one eye.

PROBLEM 191

Correct Answer

Black sacrifices a stones with 1 and gets two eyes with the moves to 9.

Wrong Answer

Without the sacrifice, it is impossible for Black to get two eyes, as the sequence to 4 shows.

PROBLEM 192

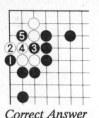

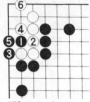

Correct Answer

The hane of Black 1 is the vital point. Black kills White's stones with the sequence to 5.

Wrong Answer

Black 1 and 3 are not the tesujis for this position. White can live with the moves 4 and 6.

PROBLEM 193

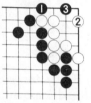

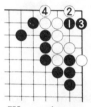

Correct Answer

Black 1 is the vital point. No matter how White plays, his stones die.

Wrong Answer

Black 1 is answered by White 2 and 4. White is now alive.

PROBLEM 194

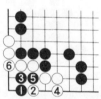

Correct Answer

Black 1 and 3 force White to play 2 and 4, but 5 creates a 4-point nakade, so White is dead.

Wrong Answer

If Black starts with 1, White can turn the corner into a ko with 2 and 4.

PROBLEM 195

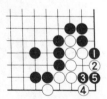

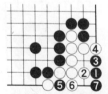

Correct Answer 1

The sequence up to Black 5 is one way to kill White's stones.

Correct Answer 2

The moves to Black 7 here are the other way to kill White.

PROBLEM 196

Correct Answer

Black 1 and 3 kill the white stones.

Wrong Answer

If Black plays 1, White gets a ko with 2 and 4.

PROBLEM 197

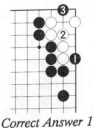

Correct Answer 1

Black can kill White by playing 1 and 3.

Correct Answer 2

Black can also kill White by playing 1 and 3 in the reverse order.

PROBLEM 198

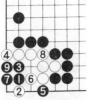

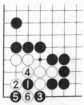

Correct Answer

Black 1 is the vital point of the 'carpenter's square'. After the moves to 9, White is dead.

Wrong Answer

Black 1 misses the vital point. White creates a ko in the corner with the moves to 6.

PROBLEM 199

Correct Answer

White creates the bent-four-in-the-corner shape with the moves to 7, so White is dead.

Wrong Answer

Black 1 is in the wrong direction. White gets two eyes and lives with 2 and 4.

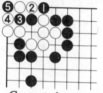
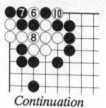

PROBLEM 200

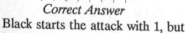

Correct Answer

Black starts the attack with 1, but White 2 and 4 are strong counters. After Black 5 —

Continuation

9: connects at 6; 11: at 7

The sequence continues until White captures six stones with 10, after which Black kills White by making a placement at the point 7 with 11.

PROBLEM 201

Correct Answer

Black 1 is the vital point. After White 2, Black sacrifices a stones with 3 and White can't get two eyes.

Wrong Answer

Sacrificing with Black 1 first is wrong. White gets two eyes with 2 and 4.

PROBLEM 202

Correct Answer

Black 1 to 5 is the correct order of moves. White is dead.

Wrong Answer

If Black plays 1 first, there is no shortage of liberties. White's stones are now unconditionally alive.

PROBLEM 203

Correct Answer

After the moves to Black 5, White can't make his second eye because of a shortage of liberties.

Wrong Answer

Black 1 is played from the wrong direction. When White plays 2, he is alive.

PROBLEM 204

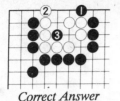

Correct Answer

Black kills White by playing the hane of 1, then destroying White's eye shape with the placement of 3.

Wrong Answer

Playing Black 1 first fails. White lives in seki with the moves to White 6.

PROBLEM 205

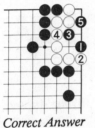

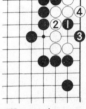

Correct Answer

Black kills White by playing the moves up to 5.

Wrong Answer

The order of moves is important. If Black 1 and 3, White lives with 4.

PROBLEM 206

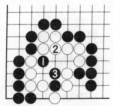

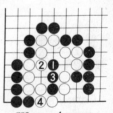

Correct Answer

If Black plays 1 and 3, White is helpless because of his shortage of liberties.

Wrong Answer

Black 1 and 3 here do not work. White lives with a seki when he connects at 4.

PROBLEM 207

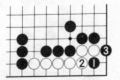

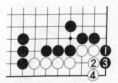

Correct Answer

Black 1 kills White by taking advantage of his shortage of liberties.

Wrong Answer

If Black plays 1, White can live with 2 and 4.

PROBLEM 208

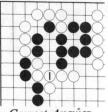

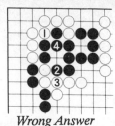

Correct Answer

If White plays 1, there is no way that Black can get a second eye.

Wrong Answer

If White ataris with 1, Black plays his own atari with 2. When White answers with 3, Black lives with 4.

PROBLEM 209

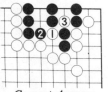

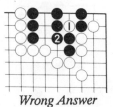

Correct Answer

White kills Black with 1 and 3. If Black 2 at 3, White plays 3 one point above 2.

Wrong Answer

If White throws in a stone at 1, Black easily gets two eyes by playing at 2.

PROBLEM 210

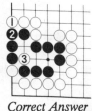

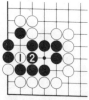

Correct Answer

White calmly plays 1. If Black 2, White destroys Black's eye shape with the atari of 3.

Wrong Answer

If White plays 1 first, Black gets two eyes when he plays 2.

PROBLEM 211

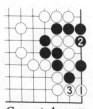

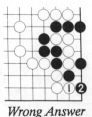

Correct Answer

White plays 1 and 3. Black captures four stones, but he can't live.

Wrong Answer

White 1 results in a ko when Black plays 2.

PROBLEM 212

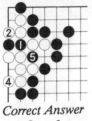

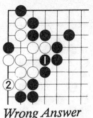

Correct Answer
3: at 1

Black sacrifices two stones with 1 and then throws in another with 3. When Black plays 5, White is dead.

Wrong Answer

Simply playing 1 enables White to get two eyes with 2.

PROBLEM 213

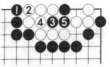

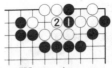

Correct Answer

Black 1 kills the white stones. If White 2, Black 3 and 5 destroy White's eye shape.

Wrong Answer

Black 1 enables White to live with 2.

PROBLEM 214

Correct Answer

Black 1 is the vital point of White's eye shape. There is now no way that White can live.

Wrong Answer

If Black plays 1, White gets a ko when he plays 2.

PROBLEM 215

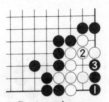

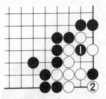

Correct Answer

Black 1 and 3 create a bent-four-in-the-corner shape, so White is dead. If 2 at 3, Black 2.

Wrong Answer

If Black tries to sacrifice a stone with 1, White can turn the corner into a ko by playing 2.

PROBLEM 216

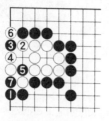

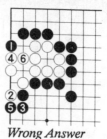

Correct Answer
Black 1 is the vital point. If White 2, the moves to 7 kill White.

Wrong Answer
If Black plays 1, White can get a ko with the moves to 6.

PROBLEM 217

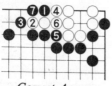

Correct Answer
The clamp of Black 1 is the vital point. By sacrificing two stones with 7, Black destroys White's second eye.

Wrong Answer
If Black plays 1, White easily gets two eyes by descending to 2.

PROBLEM 218

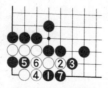

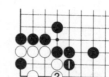

Correct Answer
The answer here is similar to the preceding problem. The final sacrifice of Black 7 kills White.

Wrong Answer
If Black plays 1, White easily gets two eyes by descending to 2.

PROBLEM 219

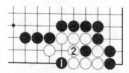

Correct Answer
Again the final sacrifice of Black 7 kills White.

Wrong Answer
Black 1 is answered by White 2. Now Black can't kill White.

PROBLEM 220

Correct Answer
Black 1 is the vital point. If White 2, Black 3 kills White.

Wrong Answer
If Black 1, White lives with 2, the vital point for making two eyes.

PROBLEM 221

Correct Answer
Black 1 is the vital point. If White 2, Black 3 kills White.

Wrong Answer
Black 1 is the wrong point. White is alive when he plays 2.

PROBLEM 222

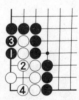

Correct Answer
Black 1 and 3 kill White.

Wrong Answer
Attaching with 1 fails. White lives by playing 2 and 4.

PROBLEM 223

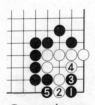

Correct Answer
The placement of Black 1 is the vital point. If White 2, Black 3 and 5 kill White.

Wrong Answer
The clamp of Black 1 fails. White lives by playing 2 and 4. If Black 3 at 4, White 4 at 3.

PROBLEM 224

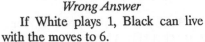

Correct Answer

If White plays 1, Black is short of liberties after the exchange of 2 for 3.

Wrong Answer

If White plays 1, Black can live with the moves to 6.

PROBLEM 225

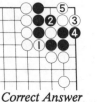

Correct Answer

White makes an eye in the corner with the moves to 5. The black stones are now dead.

Wrong Answer

If Black is allowed to play at 2, there is no way that White can kill Black.

PROBLEM 226

Correct Answer

If White plays 1, the black stones are dead.

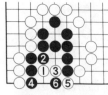

Wrong Answer

If White plays 1 here, Black lives with the moves to 6.

PROBLEM 227

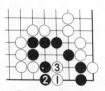

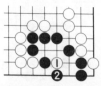

Correct Answer

The placement of White 1 is the vital point. Black's stones are dead after the exchange of 2 for 3.

Wrong Answer

Clamping with White 1 fails. It is clear that Black can get two eyes after he plays 2.

PROBLEM 228

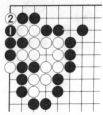

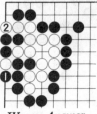

Correct Answer
3: one point below 1
Black 1 sacrifices four stones. After 3, the eye on the edge is false.

Wrong Answer
Black 1 fails. After 2, White is absolutely alive.

PROBLEM 229

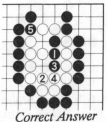

Correct Answer
Black kills White with the moves to 5. If White 2 at 3, Black 3 at 2.

Wrong Answer
Black 1 fails. White lives with 2 and 4.

PROBLEM 230

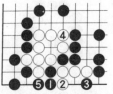

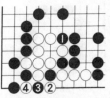

Correct Answer
The moves to 5 kill White. White takes three stones, but Black retakes and White has only a false eye.

Wrong Answer
If Black plays 1, White can create a ko at the edge with 2 and 4.

PROBLEM 231

Correct Answer
Black first plays 1, then connects at 3, creating a 5-point nakade.

Wrong Answer
If Black 1, White gets a ko with 2 and 4.

PROBLEM 232

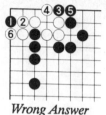

Correct Answer

The moves to Black 9 create a bent-four-in-the-corner shape. White is dead.

Wrong Answer

White can live with the moves to 6 if Black plays 1 as in this diagram.

PROBLEM 233

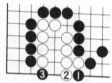

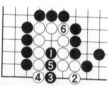

Correct Answer

Attaching with Black 1 is the vital point. After Black 5, White can't get two eyes.

Wrong Answer

Black 1 fails. After White 2, there is no way Black can stop White from living.

PROBLEM 234

Correct Answer

Black 1 and 3 kill White.

Wrong Answer

Black 1 enables White to live in seki with the moves to 6.

PROBLEM 235

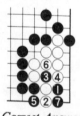

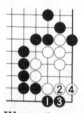

Correct Answer

The clamp of Black 1 is the vital point. White is dead when Black plays 7.

Wrong Answer

If Black plays 1, White can live with 2 and 4.

PROBLEM 236

Correct Answer
Black 1 is the vital point. Black gets a ko in the corner with the moves to 6.

Reference Diagram
Black could also get a ko with 1 and 3 here, but in an actual game, the correct answer would be more advantageous.

PROBLEM 237

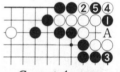

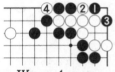

Correct Answer
The 1–2 point is again the vital point. The ko begins with 5. Even if White plays 2 at A, it is still a ko.

Wrong Answer
If Black plays 1, White is unconditionally alive after 2 and 4.

PROBLEM 238

Correct Answer
Black gets a ko with the moves to 5.

Wrong Answer
If Black 1, White is unconditionally alive when he plays 2.

PROBLEM 239

Correct Answer
Black can get an approach-move ko by playing 1 and 3.

Wrong Answer
If Black exchanges 1 for 2, White is unconditionally alive.

PROBLEM 240

Correct Answer

Black gets a ko in the corner by playing the moves to 5.

Wrong Answer

Black 1 is the standard tesuji, but because White's two stones on the 3rd line have liberties, it fails.

PROBLEM 241

Correct Answer

Black 1 is the vital point. Black gets a ko with the moves to 5.

Wrong Answer

If Black plays 1, White gets two eyes with 2 and 4.

PROBLEM 242

Correct Answer

Black 1 is the vital point. Black gets a ko with the moves to 7. If Black took a stone with 5, it would still be a ko.

Wrong Answer

If Black 1, White plays 2 on the vital point and gets two eyes with 4.

PROBLEM 243

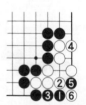

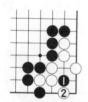

Correct Answer

Black gets a ko with the moves to 5.

Wrong Answer

Black 1 fails. White is guaranteed two eyes when he plays 2.

PROBLEM 244

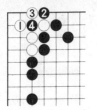

Correct Answer
White turns the corner into a ko with 1 and 3.

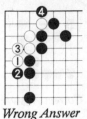

Wrong Answer
If White plays 1 and 3, Black 4 kills White's stones unconditionally.

PROBLEM 245

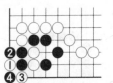

Correct Answer
White 1 is a brilliant move. Black 2 is the strongest response, but White gets a ko with 3.

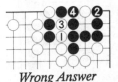

Wrong Answer
White catches two stones with 1 and 3, but Black gets two eyes with 2 and 4.

PROBLEM 246

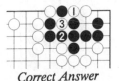

Correct Answer
White 1 is a brilliant move. If Black 2, White 3 creates the ko.

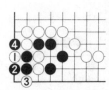

Wrong Answer
White 1 lets Black live unconditionally with 2 and 4.

PROBLEM 247

Correct Answer
White gets a ko with 1 and 3.

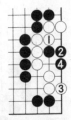

Wrong Answer
If White 1, Black creates a 5-point nakade with 2 and 4, killing White unconditionally.

PROBLEM 248

Correct Answer

Black 1 turns the corner into a ko. Either side may start the ko, but it's certain the life of the white stones will be decided by a ko.

Wrong Answer

If Black 1, White 2 turns the corner into a seki.

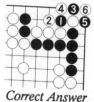

PROBLEM 249

Correct Answer

Black gets a two-step ko with the moves to 5. White 6 begins the ko.

Reference Diagram

If White plays 4, the ko becomes an immediate ko when Black plays 5.

PROBLEM 250

Correct Answer 1

Black sets up the ko with the moves to 5. He could also reverse the order of 1 and 3 and get the same ko.

Correct Answer 2

Black can also get a ko with 1, followed by the moves to 9.

PROBLEM 251

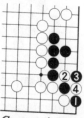

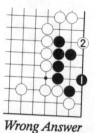

Correct Answer

Black sets up the ko with 1 and 3.

Wrong Answer

If Black 1, White 2 kills Black unconditionally.

PROBLEM 252

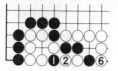

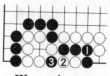

Correct Answer
3: at 1; 4: at 2; 5: right of 2;
7: takes the ko
Black gets a ko with the moves to 7, which are all forced.

Wrong Answer
4: at 2
If Black plays 1, his stones are dead when White recaptures with 4.

PROBLEM 253

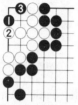

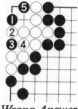

Correct Answer
Simply creating a seki with 1 and 3 is the most profitable way to play.

Wrong Answer
Sacrificing a stone with 3 is needless. This is a one-point loss for Black.

PROBLEM 254

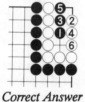

Correct Answer
If Black creates a seki with the moves to 5, he ends with sente, since White must play 6.

Wrong Answer
Creating a seki with the moves to 5 here ends in Black's gote.

PROBLEM 255

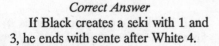

Correct Answer
If Black creates a seki with 1 and 3, he ends with sente after White 4.

Wrong Answer
Creating a seki with 1 and 3 here ends in Black's gote.

PROBLEM 256

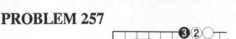

Correct Answer

If Black 1, his stones are uncon-ditionally alive in a double-ko seki.

Wrong Answer

If Black connects at 1, White can turn this into a real ko with A.

PROBLEM 257

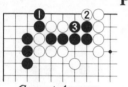

Correct Answer

Black 1 and 3 are the moves that win this capturing race for Black.

Wrong Answer

Black 1 is far away from the scene of the battle. White wins the capturing race with 2 and 4.

PROBLEM 258

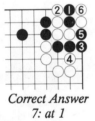

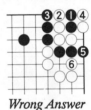

Correct Answer
7: at 1

Sacrificing two stones with 1 and then playing the moves to 7 enables Black to win the race by one move.

Wrong Answer

Atari from the other side with 3 here results in Black's losing the cap-turing race by one move.

PROBLEM 259

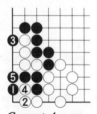

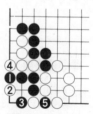

Correct Answer

Black 1 is the vital point. Black wins the capturing race by one move.

Wrong Answer

If Black 1, the corner becomes a ko with the moves to Black 5.

PROBLEM 260

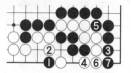

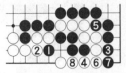

Correct Answer
Black 1 is the only move. Black will capture eight white stones by playing the moves to 7.

Wrong Answer
Black 1 misses the point. The five black stones will be captured after White plays 8.

PROBLEM 261

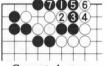

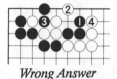

Correct Answer
Jumping to Black 1 is the only move. White's five stones will be captured after Black plays 7.

Wrong Answer
Black 1 allows White to take the vital point. Black's three stones on the right are now dead.

PROBLEM 262

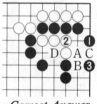

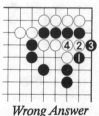

Correct Answer
Black 1 and 3 catch the four white stones. If White 2 at A, Black B, White C, Black D.

Wrong Answer
If Black 1, White will capture Black after playing 2 and 4.

PROBLEM 263

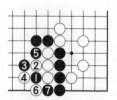

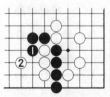

Correct Answer
If Black 1, he will capture White's four stones after the moves to 7.

Wrong Answer
Black 1 allows White to escape with the jump of 2.

PROBLEM 264

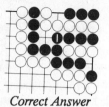

Correct Answer

If Black 1, the position is a seki. This seki, known as *hane-seki*, is one of the classic strange positions.

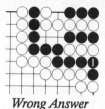

Wrong Answer

If Black captures with 1, White will play 2 in the middle of the 3-point nakade and —

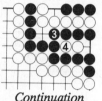

Continuation

A capturing race ensues with 3 and 4. Black loses this race because his nakade is smaller than White's.

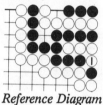

Reference Diagram

After Black 1 in the correct answer, if White plays 1, Black recaptures and the six white stones die.

PROBLEM 265

Correct Answer

If Black plays 1, the position becomes a triple ko.

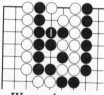

Wrong Answer

Black dies unconditionally if he plays 1. This is an example of 'one eye beats no eye'.

PROBLEM 266

Correct Answer

Black throws in a stone with 1. If White 2, Black 3 —

Wrong Answer

After White makes a ko threat, he can play 1, but then Black plays 2. When White runs out of ko threats,, Black connects a ko and wins.

PROBLEM 267

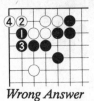

Correct Answer
Black first plays 1, then destroys White's eye shape with 3. If White 4, Black 5 is the key move.

Wrong Answer
If Black 1 and 3, White lives with 2 and 4.

PROBLEM 268

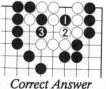

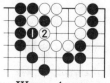

Correct Answer
Black strikes at the vital point of 1, then kills White with 3.

Wrong Answer
If Black plays 1, White gets eye shape with 2.

PROBLEM 269

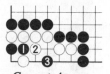

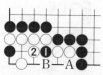

Correct Answer
Black plays 1 followed by 3. White has no counter because he is short of liberties.

Wrong Answer
If Black 1, White is alive when he plays 2. If Black 1 at A, White lives by playing B.

PROBLEM 270

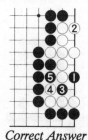

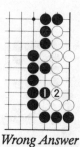

Correct Answer
Black 1 and 3 are the key moves. Black 5 now catches the four white stones below in a snapback.

Wrong Answer
Exchanging Black 1 for 2 is meaningless. White now easily gets two eyes no matter what Black does.

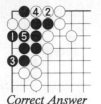

PROBLEM 271

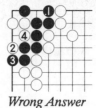

Correct Answer

Black secures two eyes with the moves to 5.

Wrong Answer

If Black 1, White turns the corner into a ko with 2 and 4.

PROBLEM 272

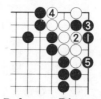

Correct Answer

If Black plays 1 and 3, White can live only by winning the ko starting with 4.

Reference Diagram

If White tries to stop the ko with 2 and 4, he is defenseless after 5 because he is short of liberties.

PROBLEM 273

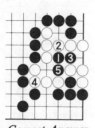

Correct Answer

Black 1 is the vital point. If White 2, Black 3 kills White.

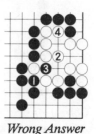

Wrong Answer

If Black 1, White 2 turns the corner into a ko. If Black 1 at A, White B and the corner is again a ko.

PROBLEM 274

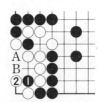

Correct Answer

Black destroys White's eye shape with the moves to 5. White is dead.

Wrong Answer

If Black 1, White gets two eyes with 2 and 4.

PROBLEM 275

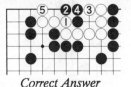

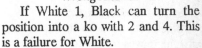

Correct Answer

White can live by turning the position into a seki with the moves to 5. If Black 2 at 4, White 3 at 5.

Wrong Answer

If White 1, Black can turn the position into a ko with 2 and 4. This is a failure for White.

PROBLEM 276

Correct Answer 1

White 1 threatens to make eyes in two directions. If Black 2, 3 gives White two eyes.

Correct Answer 2

Black 2 destroys White's eye on the right, but White gets two eyes with the moves to 7.

PROBLEM 277

Correct Answer
6: connects

By playing the moves to 7, White kills Black by creating a 5-point nakade.

Wrong Answer

The shape created by Black 1 and 3 cannot prevent Black from getting two eyes. Black is alive.

PROBLEM 278

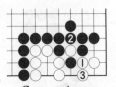

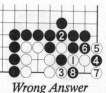

Correct Answer

Black gets a second eye in the corner by playing 1 and 3.

Wrong Answer

If White captures with 3, Black can turn this position into a ko with the moves to 8.

PROBLEM 279

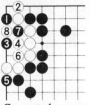

Correct Answer

Black sets up a ko in the corner with the moves from 1 to 7.

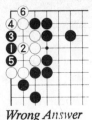

Wrong Answer

If Black plays the moves to 5, all of White's stones are alive after 6.

PROBLEM 280

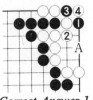

Correct Answer 1

Black sets up a ko with the moves to 3. If White 2 at 3, Black 3 at A.

Correct Answer 2

If White answers 1 with 2, Black can also set up a ko with 3 and 5.

PROBLEM 281

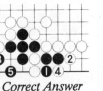

Correct Answer

If Black 1, White ataris with 2. Instead of taking two stones, Black next plays 3 and 5, sacrificing three stones but making two eyes.

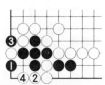

Wrong Answer

If Black plays 1, White kills all the black stones with 2 and 4.

PROBLEM 282

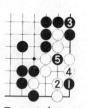

Correct Answer

Black 1 is the vital point. After 3 and 5, White's stones are dead.

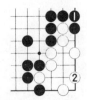

Wrong Answer

If Black connects at 1 first, White plays 2 on the vital point and is alive.

PROBLEM 283

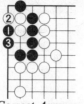

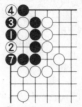

Correct Answer
If Black plays 1 and 3, he is alive in seki.

Reference Diagram
5: retakes; 6: at 1
If White answers 1 with 2, Black captures all the white stones.

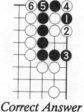

PROBLEM 284

Correct Answer
Black get a ko with the moves to 6. Compare this problem with the preceding one.

Reference Diagram
The correct answer results in a ten-thousand-year ko. If Black want a real ko, he will attach with 3.

PROBLEM 285

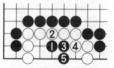

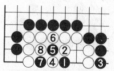

Correct Answer
Black kills White by making a 5-point nakade with the moves to 5.

Wrong Answer
If Black 1, White lives by playing the moves to 8.

PROBLEM 286

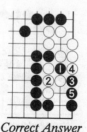

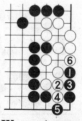

Correct Answer
Black kills White with the moves to 5.

Wrong Answer
If Black first attaches at 1, White lives with the moves to 6.

PROBLEM 287

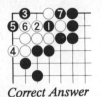

Correct Answer

The moves to Black 5 create a bent-four-in-the-corner shape, so White is dead.

Wrong Answer

Reversing the order of 1 and 3 results in White's getting two eyes with the moves to 6

PROBLEM 288

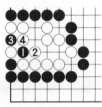

Correct Answer

Black jumps in to 1 and destroys White's eye shape with the moves to 5.

Wrong Answer

Black 1 enables White to live with 2. The sequence in the correct answer is the only way.

PROBLEM 289

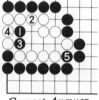

Correct Answer

Black kills White with the moves to 5.

Wrong Answer

If Black ataris with 1, White lives with 2 and 4.

PROBLEM 290

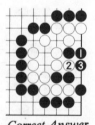

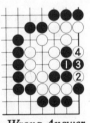

Correct Answer

Black destroys White's eye shape with 1 and 3.

Wrong Answer

If Black connects at 1, White will get a ko with 2 and 4.

PROBLEM 291

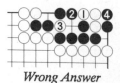

Correct Answer 1

Black kills White with the moves to 5.

Correct Answer 2

If Black answers White 1 with 2, White 3 and 5 will also kill the black stones.

PROBLEM 292

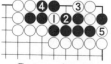

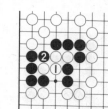

Correct Answer

White 1 to 5 is the correct order of moves. Black is dead.

Wrong Answer

Reversing the order of 1 and 3 lets Black live with 2 and 4.

PROBLEM 293

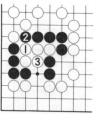

Correct Answer

White kills Black by creating a 5-point nakade with 1 and 3.

Wrong Answer

Again the order of moves is important. If White 1, Black gets a living shape when he plays 2.

PROBLEM 294

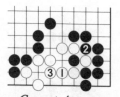

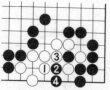

Correct Answer

White 1 is the vital point for making two eyes. If Black 2 at 3, White 3 at 2. Either way White lives.

Wrong Answer

White 1 fails. Black 2 and 4 leave White's group with only one eye.

PROBLEM 295

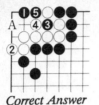

Correct Answer

Black plays the moves to 5. After White A, the life of the white stones depends on winning the ko.

Wrong Answer

If Black plays 1 and 3, White lives unconditionally with 2 and 4.

PROBLEM 296

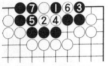

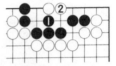

Correct Answer

After the moves to 7, White can't create a 5-point nakade by filling at 1 because he is short of liberties.

Wrong Answer

If Black plays 1, he is dead after White plays 2.

PROBLEM 297

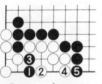

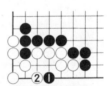

Correct Answer

Black kills White with the moves to 5.

Wrong Answer

Black 1 misses the vital point. White is alive after he plays 2.

PROBLEM 298

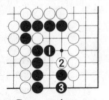

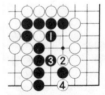

Correct Answer

Black 1 and 3 are the only way for Black to live.

Wrong Answer

If Black captures with 1, White kills Black with 2 and 4.

PROBLEM 299

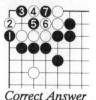

Correct Answer

Black turns the corner into a ko with the moves to 7.

Reference Diagram

Black can also get a ko with the moves to 7. Black 1 at 5 also creates a ko.

PROBLEM 300

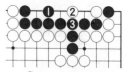

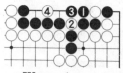

Correct Answer

Black 1 is the vital point for making two eyes. If White 2, Black plays 3 and gets his second eye.

Wrong Answer

If Black captures with 1, Black is left with only one eye after White 4.

PROBLEM 301

Correct Answer

To kill White, Black must play 1 and 3 in this order.

Wrong Answer

Throwing in with 1 first enables White to get two eyes with 2 and 4.

PROBLEM 302

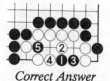

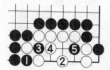

Correct Answer

Black first plays on the vital point with 1, then destroys White's eye shape with 1 and 3.

Wrong Answer

If Black 1, the best Black can do is to get a ko with the moves to 5.

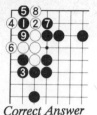
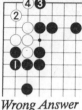

PROBLEM 303

Correct Answer

Black 1 is the vital point. After White 2, Black destroys White's eye shape with the moves to 9.

Wrong Answer

If Black connects at 1, White gets two eyes with 2 and 4.

PROBLEM 304

Correct Answer

If Black plays 1 and 3, White will only be able to get one eye after he captures the three black stones.

Wrong Answer

Black 1 and 3 are too slow. After Black captures with 4, he can easily get his second eye.

PROBLEM 305

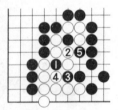
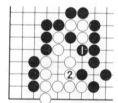

Correct Answer

Black must sacrifice a stone with 1. After the moves to Black 5, White is left with only one eye.

Wrong Answer

If Black captures three stones with 1, White can make his second eye with 2.

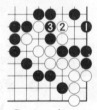

PROBLEM 306

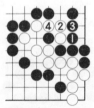

Correct Answer

Black 1 is the only move that enables Black to rescue his four stones and kill all of White's.

Wrong Answer

If Black 1, White 2 forces Black to defend at 3, so White gets his second eye with 4.

PROBLEM 307

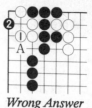

Correct Answer
White 1 and 3 give White two eyes.

Wrong Answer
If White 1, Black destroys White's eye shape with 2. If White 1 at A, Black 2 also kills White.

PROBLEM 308

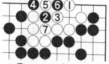

Correct Answer
White makes an open connection with 1. If Black 2, White gets two eyes with 3 and 5.

Wrong Answer
Descending to 1 lets Black capture two stones with the moves to 6, leaving White with only one eye.

PROBLEM 309

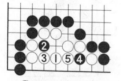

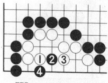

Correct Answer
White 1 is the vital point. After Black 2 and 4, White gets two eyes for his group with 5.

Wrong Answer
White 1 is bad shape. Black strikes at the vital point with 2 and kills White with 4.

PROBLEM 310

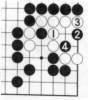

Correct Answer
White gets his two eyes by playing the moves to 5.

Wrong Answer
If White 1, Black destroys White's other eye on the right with 2 and 4.

PROBLEM 311

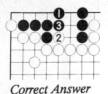

Correct Answer
Again a move on the first line is the key. Black has two eyes when he plays at 3.

Wrong Answer
If Black plays 1, the moves to White 6 create a 5-point nakade inside Black's group.

PROBLEM 312

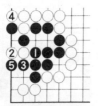

Correct Answer
Black makes two eyes for his group by playing the moves to 5.

Wrong Answer
If Black 1, White strikes at the vital point with 2 and kills Black.

PROBLEM 313

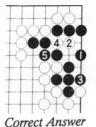

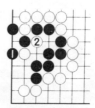

Correct Answer
Black plays 1. If White 2, Black 3 and 5 capture two stones.

Wrong Answer
If Black 1, White 2 kills the black stones. The correct answer is the only way for Black to live.

PROBLEM 314

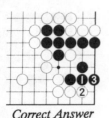

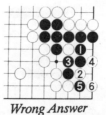

Correct Answer
Black can get eye shape and live unconditionally with 1 and 3.

Wrong Answer
If Black captures a stone with 1 and 3, White gets a ko with 4 and 6.

PROBLEM 315

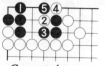

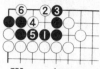

Correct Answer

Black gets two eyes with the moves to 5.

Wrong Answer

Black 1 lets White kill Black by creating a 5-point nakade with the moves to 6.

PROBLEM 316

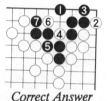

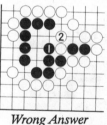

Correct Answer

Black 1 is the vital point. White tries to kill Black with the moves to 6, but Black is alive when he plays 7.

Wrong Answer

If Black 1, White kills Black with the moves to 6.

PROBLEM 317

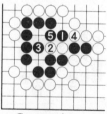

Correct Answer

Black sacrifices two stones with 1 and 3, but gets his eyes with 5.

Wrong Answer

Black has only one eye if he ataris with 1.

PROBLEM 318

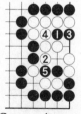

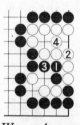

Correct Answer

Black kills White by sacrificing two stones with the moves to 5.

Wrong Answer

Black captures two white stones with 1 and 3, but the main body of White's group lives with 2 and 4.

PROBLEM 319

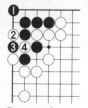

Correct Answer

Black 1 is the vital point. Black can live if he wins the ko White starts with 4.

Wrong Answer

If Black 1, White kills Black by making a bent-four-in-the-corner.

PROBLEM 320

Correct Answer

The moves to Black 5 are the only way to kill White.

Wrong Answer

If Black plays 1 and 3, White lives with 2 and 4.

PROBLEM 321

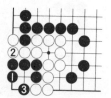

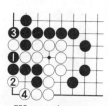

Correct Answer

Black makes two eyes in the corner with 1 and 3 and kills White. If White 2 at 3, Black 3 at 2.

Wrong Answer

Black can rescue his four stones with 1 and 3, but White gets a second eye for his stones with 2 and 4.

PROBLEM 322

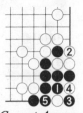

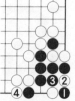

Correct Answer

Black makes two eyes and lives by playing the moves to 5.

Wrong Answer

If Black 1, the best Black can get is a ko after White 4.

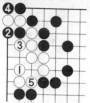

PROBLEM 323

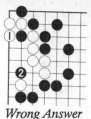

Correct Answer

White 1 is the vital point for making two eyes. Black captures two stones, but White lives with 3 and 5.

Wrong Answer

Capturing a black stone with 1 fails. Black strikes at the vital point with 2, and White can't get two eyes.

PROBLEM 324

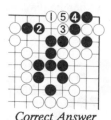

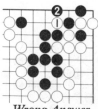

Correct Answer

White can kill Black with the moves to 5.

Wrong Answer

If White ataris with 1, Black can get a ko with 2.

PROBLEM 325

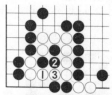

Correct Answer

White 1 and 3 enable White's stones to live. Black captures three stones and two stones with one move.

Wrong Answer
4: at 2

White 3 fails. Black 4 leaves White with only one eye.

PROBLEM 326

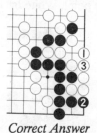

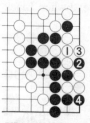

Correct Answer

White 1 is the only way to kill Black. If Black captures two stones with 4, White retakes one stone.

Wrong Answer

If White connects with 1, Black lives by capturing three stones with 2 and 4.

PROBLEM 327

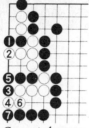

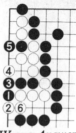

Correct Answer

If Black descends to 1, he can capture White's stones with the moves to 7.

Wrong Answer

The order of moves is important. If Black plays 1 and 3 before 5, White lives when he plays 6.

PROBLEM 328

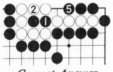

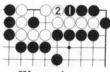

Correct Answer

3: at 1; 4: captures a stone

Black sacrifices two stones with 1, then another with 3. 5 kills White.

Wrong Answer

White lives if Black plays 1. The sacrifices in the correct answer keep White short of liberties.

PROBLEM 329

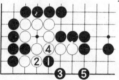

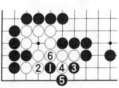

Correct Answer

Black 1 strikes at the vital point. White is dead when Black plays 5.

Wrong Answer

Black 1 is a good move, but 3 misses the point. White lives with 6.

PROBLEM 330

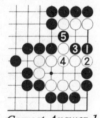

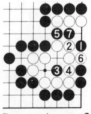

Correct Answer 1

Black 1 and 3 are correct. If White 4, Black 5 kills White.

Correct Answer 2

If White plays 2 in answer to 1, the moves to Black 7 kill White.

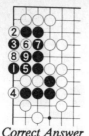

PROBLEM 331

Correct Answer
Black 1 catches two white stones. If White tries to prevent Black from getting a second eye, Black will capture two stones after he plays 9.

Wrong Answer
If Black plays 1, the moves to White 6 leave Black with only one eye.

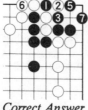

PROBLEM 332

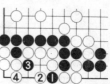

Correct Answer
4: connects at 1
If Black sacrifices a stone with 1, he gets two eyes with the moves to 7.

Wrong Answer
If Black simply plays 1, he has no follow-up moves to live after White 2.

PROBLEM 333

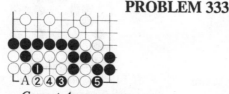

Correct Answer
After 1 and 3, White must give up the three stones in atari. If he connects, A kills all of White's stones.

Wrong Answer
The order of moves is important. Playing 1 first allows White to live with all of his stones.

PROBLEM 334

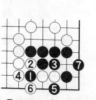

Correct Answer
Black can make two eyes by playing 1 and the moves to 7.

Wrong Answer
Simply playing 1 and 3 fails to get two eyes. White 4 kills Black.

PROBLEM 335

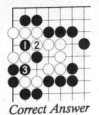

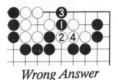

Correct Answer

Black 1 is the vital point. If White 2, Black 3 kills White.

Wrong Answer

Black cannot reverse the order of moves with 1 and 3. If he does, White lives when he captures with 4.

PROBLEM 336

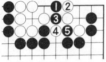

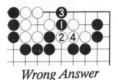

Correct Answer

Black kills White with the moves to 5. If White 2 at 3, Black 3 at 2.

Wrong Answer

If Black plays 1, White will live with 2 and 4.

PROBLEM 337

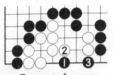

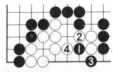

Correct Answer

Black 1 is the vital point. If White 2, Black 3 kills White.

Wrong Answer

If Black 1 and 3, White gets two eyes with 2 and 4.

PROBLEM 338

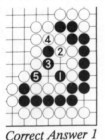

Correct Answer 1

Black captures three stones with the moves to 5. Now Black's stones are alive.

Correct Answer 2

If White answers Black 1 with 2, Black will capture four white stones with the moves to 5.

PROBLEM 339

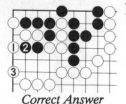

Correct Answer

White plays 1. If Black 2, White plays 3, sacrificing two stones. Black is dead.

Wrong Answer

If White 1, Black catches four white stones with the moves to 4.

PROBLEM 340

Correct Answer

White 1 is a brilliancy. After Black 2, White plays 3 and 5, capturing two stones and getting two eyes.

Wrong Answer

If White 1, Black kills all the black stones with 2 and 4.

PROBLEM 341

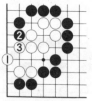

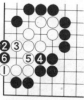

Correct Answer

White 1 is the vital point for making a second eye.

Wrong Answer

If White 1, Black kills White with the moves to 6.

PROBLEM 342

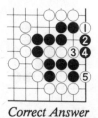

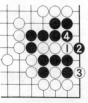

Correct Answer

White first plays 1, then increases the sacrifice to three stones with 3. After White 5, Black is dead.

Wrong Answer

Playing 1 first results in Black's getting two eyes with 2 and 4.

PROBLEM 343

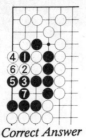

Correct Answer

Black sacrifices a stone with 1 and lives with the moves to 7.

Wrong Answer

Black 1 is too slow. After 2, there is no way that Black can get two eyes.

PROBLEM 344

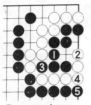

Correct Answer

The moves to Black 5 kill all the white stones.

Wrong Answer

If Black 1, White can live by capturing four black stones with 2 and 4.

PROBLEM 345

Correct Answer

If Black plays 1 and 3, he can capture five stones in a snapback with 5, killing all the white stones.

Wrong Answer

If Black 1 and 3, White can live with 2 and 4.

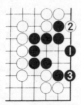

PROBLEM 346

Correct Answer

Black can get two eyes by playing 1 and 3. If White 2 at 3, Black 3 at 2, and Black again has two eyes.

Wrong Answer

If Black reverses the order of moves as here, White destroys Black's eye shape with 2 and 4.

PROBLEM 347

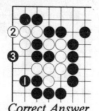

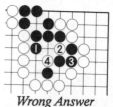

Correct Answer
White kills Black with 1 and 3.

Wrong Answer
If Black 1, White is alive after he captures three stones with 2.

PROBLEM 348

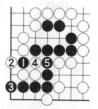

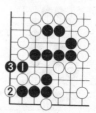

Correct Answer
Black 1 is the vital point for Black's second eye.

Wrong Answer
If Black 1, White throws in a stone with 2 and kills Black with 4.

PROBLEM 349

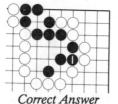

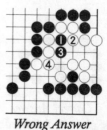

Correct Answer 1
Black gets his second eye in the corner with the moves to 5.

Correct Answer 2
If White plays 2 in answer to 1, Black 3 will catch the three white stones in the corner.

PROBLEM 350

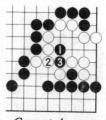

Correct Answer
Black kills White with the moves to 3.

Wrong Answer
Black 1 and 3 fail. White lives with 4.

PROBLEM 351

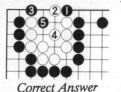

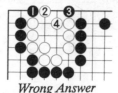

Correct Answer

Playing from the right with 1 is correct. White is dead after Black 5.

Wrong Answer

Black 1 here fails. White lives with 2 and 4.

PROBLEM 352

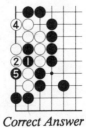

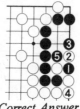

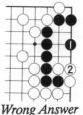

Correct Answer

Black can make eye shape by sacrificing with 1 and playing 3 and 5.

Wrong Answer

If Black 1, he is dead after White 2. Black must sacrifice a stone to live.

PROBLEM 353

Correct Answer
3: at 1

Black sacrifices two stones with 1, then another with 3. White is dead after Black plays 5.

Wrong Answer

If Black 1, White plays 2 and gets two eyes.

PROBLEM 354

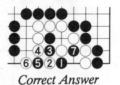

Correct Answer

Black plays 1, followed by 3 and 5. After White 6, Black 7 captures two white stones.

Wrong Answer

The order of moves is important. If Black plays 1 and 3, the position turns into a ko with White 8.

PROBLEM 355

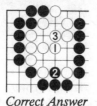

Correct Answer

White 1 threatens to make eyes in two places. If Black 2 at 3, White 3 at 2, and White still has two eyes.

Wrong Answer

If White 1, Black plays 2 on the vital point and White is dead.

PROBLEM 356

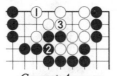

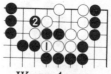

Correct Answer

White lives with 1 and 3.

Wrong Answer

If White immediately cuts off the two black stones with 1, Black plays 2, so White is left with a false eye.

PROBLEM 357

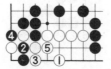

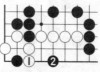

Correct Answer

White 1 is the vital point for making two eyes. White then lives with the moves to 5.

Wrong Answer

If White tries to save all his stones with 1, Black plays 2 and White has only one eye.

PROBLEM 358

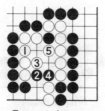

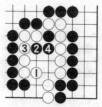

Correct Answer

White 1 is the vital point. If Black 2, White lives with 3 and 5.

Wrong Answer

If White 1, Black kills White by making a 4-point nakade with 2 to 4.

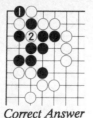

PROBLEM 359

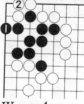

Correct Answer

Throwing in a stone with 1 creates a ko, which is the only way Black can live.

Wrong Answer

If Black 1, White connects at 2 and Black has only one eye. Black is unconditionally dead.

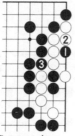

PROBLEM 360

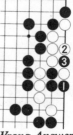

Correct Answer

Black kills White with the moves 1 and 3.

Wrong Answer

If Black 1, White 2 turns the position into a ko.

PROBLEM 361

Correct Answer

Black kills White by playing the moves to 7. White can't do anything because he is short of liberties.

Wrong Answer

If Black 1, White can get two eyes with the moves to 6.

PROBLEM 362

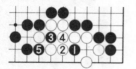

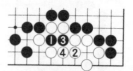

Correct Answer

Black kills White by playing 1 and 3. After Black 5, White can get only one eye.

Wrong Answer

If Black 1, White gives up two stones and takes the vital point at 2. With 4, White gets his second eye.

— 190 —

PROBLEM 363

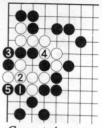

Correct Answer

Black kills all the white stones with the moves to 6.

Wrong Answer

If Black 1, White can catch the black stones with the moves to 6.

PROBLEM 364

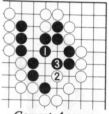

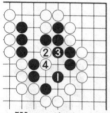

Correct Answer

Black 1 is the vital point. If White 2, Black has two eyes after playing 3.

Wrong Answer

If Black 1, White plays 2 and 4, killing the black stones.

PROBLEM 365

Correct Answer

After the moves to Black 5, White can't counterattack because he is short of liberties.

Wrong Answer

If Black plays 1 first, White can get a ko with 2.

PROBLEM 366

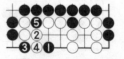

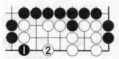

Correct Answer

White creates a shortage of liberties with the moves to 5, killing all the white stones.

Wrong Answer

Black 1 lets White to get a second eye by playing 2. White is now alive.

— 191 —

PROBLEM 367

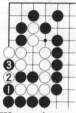

Correct Answer

Black kills White with the moves to 5.

Wrong Answer

If Black 1, White throws in a stone with 2, and the position becomes a ko. Black has failed.

PROBLEM 368

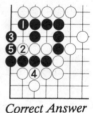

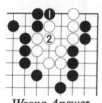

Correct Answer

Black kills White with 1 and 3.

Wrong Answer

If Black 1, White gets two eyes by playing at 2.

PROBLEM 369

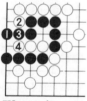

Correct Answer

Black lives by creating a seki with the moves to 5.

Wrong Answer

If Black 1, White kills Black with 2 and 4.

PROBLEM 370

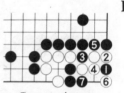

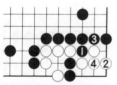

Correct Answer

If Black plays the moves to 7, White is dead. He has no way to move because he is short of liberties.

Wrong Answer

If Black 1, White is alive after he plays 2 and 4.

PROBLEM 371

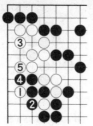

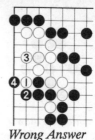

Correct Answer
White 1 is the vital point. White gets two eyes with the moves to 5.

Wrong Answer
If White plays 1 and 3, Black turns the position into a ko with 4.

PROBLEM 372

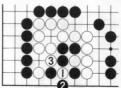

Correct Answer
White gets two eyes with the moves to 3.

Wrong Answer
White 1 is not sente! White is left without any eyes after Black plays 6.

PROBLEM 373

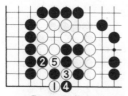

Correct Answer
White captures three black stones and gets two eyes with the moves to 5.

Wrong Answer
4: connects at 1
This order of moves is wrong. After Black 4, there is no way White can capture any black stones.

PROBLEM 374

Correct Answer
White can live by playing 1 and 3.

Wrong Answer
If White 1 and 3, Black kills White by creating a 5-point nakade with 2 and 4.

PROBLEM 375

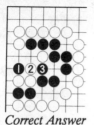

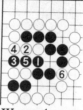

Correct Answer

Black 1 is a brilliant tesuji. If White 2, Black catches the white stone with 3.

Wrong Answer

The order of moves is important. Black can capture two stones up to 5, but after 6 he has only one eye.

PROBLEM 376

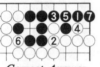

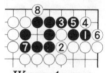

Correct Answer

Black 1 is the vital point. Black gets eyes with the moves to 7.

Wrong Answer

Black 1 fails. White kills Black with the moves to 8. Black 1 at 5 also fails after White plays 2.

PROBLEM 377

Correct Answer

Black 1 is the vital point. White is dead after Black plays 3.

Wrong Answer

If Black plays 1, White gets two eyes with 2 and 4.

PROBLEM 378

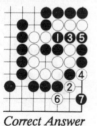

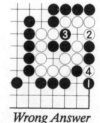

Correct Answer

Black lets White capture a stone with 2 and 4, but all the white stones are dead after Black plays 7.

Wrong Answer

If Black defends with 1, White lives in seki with the moves to 4.

PROBLEM 379

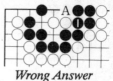

Correct Answer

Black lives in seki with 1 and 3. If White A, Black B.

Wrong Answer

If Black plays either 1 or A, the position becomes a 5-point nakade.

PROBLEM 380

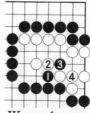

Correct Answer

Black 1 is the vital point. After the moves to 7, White is dead.

Wrong Answer

If Black 1 and 3, White lives with 4. If Black 1 at 3, White plays 2.

PROBLEM 381

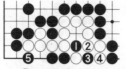

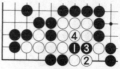

Correct Answer
6: takes ko

Black 1 and White 2 are the moves you have to find. White starts the ko with 6.

Wrong Answer
5: at 3

White 2 here is a mistake. Black kills White unconditionally with 3 and 5.

PROBLEM 382

Correct Answer

Black gets two eyes with 1 and 3.

Wrong Answer
4: throws in; 5: takes; 7: connects

Black 1 here is unreasonable. White kills Black up to 8.

PROBLEM 383

Correct Answer

Black sacrifices a stone with 1 and lives by getting a double ko with the moves to 5.

Wrong Answer

Black 1 is a mistake. White plays 2 and it becomes a simple ko that Black has to win to live.

PROBLEM 384

Correct Answer

Black plays two hanes with 1 and 3. With the double ko beginning at 5, White dies.

Wrong Answer

If Black answers 2 with 3, when White plays 4, it becomes a simple ko that Black must win to kill White.

PROBLEM 385

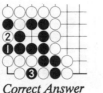

Correct Answer

Black 1 turns this into a double ko. White's stones will now be captured by Black.

Wrong Answer
4: takes ko

If Black 1, White exchanges 2 for 3 and goes back to take the ko with 4. White can live by winning this ko.

PROBLEM 386

Correct Answer

Black can get an approach-move ko with 1 and 3. If White 2 at 3, Black A gives a ko.

Wrong Answer

Black 1 and 3 let White live unconditionally with 2 and 4.

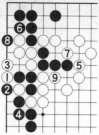

PROBLEM 387

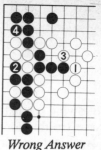

Correct Answer

White 1 and 3 increase White's liberties by one. White wins the capturing race with the moves to 9.

Wrong Answer

If White plays 1 and 3, he loses the capturing race by one move.

PROBLEM 388

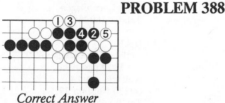

Correct Answer

White 1 is the vital point. After the moves to 5, it is clear that the black stones will be captured.

Wrong Answer

White 1 is too slow. Black now wins the capturing race by one move.

PROBLEM 389

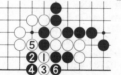
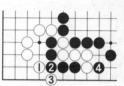

Correct Answer
7: at 1

White wins the capturing race by playing the moves to 7.

Wrong Answer

White 1 and 3 fail. After Black 4, it is clear that Black wins the capturing race by one move.

PROBLEM 390

Correct Answer
5: takes ko at 1

White throws in a stone with 1 and starts a ko with 5.

Wrong Answer

If White plays 1 and 3, Black wins the capturing race by one move.

GO ASSOCIATIONS

The following is a list of national go associations throughout the world. If you have trouble locating other go players in your community, your local go organization may be able to help you.

ARGENTINA
Argentina Go Association
c/o Mr. Guillermo E. Zucal
Aroz 2730 -6o,
1425 Capital Federal
Tel. 71-3182

AUSTRALIA
Australian Go Association,
c/o Bill Leveritt,
"Denmora",
20 Cowlishaw Street,
Bowen Hills, QLD, 4006

AUSTRIA
Osterreichischer Go-Verband,
c/o Dr. Alfred Kriegler,
1030 Wien,
Rechte Bahngasse 28/2,
Tel. 7238335

BRAZIL
Brazil Ki-in
c/o Mr. Toshikatsu Takamori,
Rua Maria Figueiredo,
350 Sao Paulo,
Tel. 289-4062

CANADA
Canadian Go Association,
c/o Mr. Tibor Bognar,
8982 St. Hubert,
Montreal, Quebec H2M 1Y6
Tel. 387-1646

CHINA
China Weiqi Association,
Ti-yu-guan Lu 9,
Peking, Tel. 753110

CZECHOSLOVAKIA
Czechoslovak Go Association,
c/o Dr. Dusan Prokop,
Laubova 8,
130-00 Praha 3, CSSR
Tel. 276565

DENMARK
Denmark Go Association,
c/o Mr. Frank Hansen,
Nordre Frihavnsgade 24,
2100 Copenhagen,
Tel. 01-269460

FINLAND
Finland Go Association,
c/o Mr. Keijo Alho,
Kuusitie 8 A 14,
00270 Helsinki 27,
Tel. 90-483401

FRANCE
Federation Francaise de Go,
B.P. 9506,
75262 Paris Cedex 06

F. R. GERMANY
Deutscher Go Bund,
c/o Mr. Martin Stiassny,
Am Burgturm 2,
D-4048 Grevenbroich I,
Tel. 02181-42021

HONG KONG
Hong Kong Go Club,
458 Nathan Road,
8th Floor, B Flat,
Kowloon,
Tel. 3-857728

HUNGARY
Hungary Go Association,
c/o Mr. Gacs Istvan,
H-1085 Budapest,
Saletrom 6

ITALY
Italian Go Association,
c/o Raffaele Rinaldi,
Via La Marmora 18,
Milano,
Tel. 02-581523

JAPAN
Nihon Ki-in,
7-2 Gobancho,
Chiyoda-ku, Tokyo 102,
Tel. 03-262-6161

KOREA
Korea Baduk Association,
13-4. Kwanchul-Dong,
Chongro-gu, Seoul,
Tel. 723-0150

MEXICO
Mexican Go Association,
c/o Mr. Carlos Torres,
Watteau 15-2, Col. Nonoalco,
Delegacion Benito Juarez 03720
Tel. 563-2302

NETHERLANDS
Dutch Go Association,
c/o Mr. J. H. van Frankenhuysen,
J. Verhulststraat 125,
1071 NA Amsterdam
Tel. 020-739232

NEW ZEALAND
National Seretary, N. Z. Go Society,
c/o Mr. Peter Rochford,
Victoria University, Private Bag,
Wellington
Tel. (Home) 727267

NORWAY
Norwegian Go Association,
c/o Mr. Morten Skogen,
Kzempeveien 13E,
N-4600 Kristiansand Syd,
Tel. 42-91373

POLAND
Warsaw Go Club,
c/o Mr. Leszek Dziumowicz,
Nowy Swiat 47/3a,
P00-042 Warszawa

RUMANIA
c/o Mr. Gheorghe Paun,
Institute of Mathematics Str.,
Academiei 14,
70109 Bucuresti
Tel. (Home) 256754

SINGAPORE
Singapore Go Association,
c/o Mr. Gin Hor Chan,
Dept. of Mathematics,
National University of Singapore
Kent Ridge, Singapore 0511,
Tel. 7756666, Ext. 2083

SPAIN
Spanish Go Association,
c/o Mr. Ambrosio Wang An-Po,
Vallehermoso 89,
Madrid

SWEDEN
The Swedish Go Association,
c/o Mr. Per-Inge Olsson,
Safirgangen 24,
S-13 549 Tyreso,
Tel. 08-770-0927

SWITZERLAND
Swiss Go Federation,
c/o Mr. Tamotsu Takase,
20 Ch. des Grangettes,
1224 Chene-bougerie, Geneve,
Tel. 489541

TAIWAN
Chinese Taipei Wei-ch'i Association,
c/o Mr. C. S. Shen,
4th Fl., Kuang Fu Building,
No. 35 Kuang Fu S. Rd.,
Taipei, Taiwan R. O. C.
Tel. 7614117

UNITED KINGDOM
British Go Association,
c/o Mr. Norman R. Tobin,
10 West Common Road,
Uxbridge, Middlesex UB8 1NZ,
Tel. 0895-30511

USA
American Go Association
P. O. Box 397,
Old Chelsea Station,
New York, N. Y. 10011

YUGOSLAVIA
Go Savez Jugoslavije,
c/o Mr. Peter Gaspari,
Aleseva 3, 61210 Ljubljana –
Sentvid. Tel. (061) 52-111